Longman Science homework for Edexcel IGCSE
Answer book

Ann Fullick, Patrick Fullick and Martin Stirrup

PEARSON

Longman

Pearson Education
Edinburgh Gate
Harlow
Essex
CM20 2JE

and Associated Companies throughout the world

www.longman.co.uk

ISBN: 978 1 4058 7494 6

Development and editorial by Sue Kearsey
Designed by Redmoor Design, Tavistock, Devon
Cover photo ©www.istockphoto.com
Printed in Great Britain by Henry Ling Ltd., at the Dorset Press. Dorchester, Dorset

Contents

How to use this book

Regular set homework is important to a student's learning. Research has shown that homework can give the equivalent input to a student's education of an extra year at school. However, there are often problems that make this important aim difficult to achieve. It may not be possible to send books home, and homework question sheets are time-consuming to prepare, of variable quality and easily lost. The Homework Books are designed to overcome these problems.

The homework sheets link to the chapters in the *Longman ... for IGCSE* series. The contents list in each Homework Book shows how the sheets link to the Student Books. They also cover the Edexcel IGCSE separate science specifications, and the specification matching grids in this Answer Book show how the homework sheets cover the content of each specification.

The questions in the Homework Books are graded, starting with simple exercises and increasing in difficulty as appropriate to the topic. Higher Tier material is clearly marked, and covers material up to and including A* grade. Some questions expect a small amount of recall, but sufficient background information is included with questions so that students don't need access to the Student's Book to answer them.

A variety of question styles has been used. Some questions test students' knowledge and understanding. However, the primary purpose it to encourage students to reprocess and record information and ideas.

Activities such as cloze procedures, sequencing exercises and annotated diagrams encourage long-term memory development. They also lead students to record key information which will be useful for revision.

The higher level questions encourage understanding of key concepts using structured questioning and/or analogy. Calculations are also introduced where appropriate, again becoming increasingly more difficult.

Data analysis and response questions expect students to extract information from tables, charts and graphs, and to spot and describe relationships and patterns. More general questions encourage students to develop their scientific understanding within social and environmental contexts,

This Answer Book provides full answers for all questions in the Homework Books.

Biology

Specification matching grid		
Section	**Content**	**Worksheets**
I The nature and variety of living organisms		
a Characteristics of living organisms	• basic characteristics of living organisms	I, 2
b Variety of living organisms	• wide variety of living organisms common features shared within plants, animals, fungi, bacteria and viruses	5
2 Structures and functions in living organisms		
a Levels of organisation	• levels of organisation within organisms	I, 2
b Cell structure	• cell structures • functions of some cell structures • differences between plant and animal cells	I
c Biological molecules	• chemical elements in carbohydrates, proteins and lipids (fats and oils) • the structure of carbohydrates, proteins and lipids • *tests for glucose, starch, lipid and protein* • role of enzymes • enzyme function and temperature and pH • *experiments on enzyme activity and temperature*	3, 10
d Movement of substances into and out of cells	• diffusion, osmosis and active transport • turgid cells • **effects of surface area to volume ratio, temperature and concentration gradient** • *simple experiments on diffusion and osmosis*	4, 10, 25
e Nutrition Flowering plants	• photosynthesis • equations for photosynthesis • factors that affect the rate of photosynthesis • how the leaf is adapted for photosynthesis • plants require mineral ions for growth • *experiments to investigate photosynthesis*	21, 22, 23, 24
e Nutrition Humans	• balanced diet • sources and functions of various nutrients • energy requirements vary • structures of the human alimentary canal and their functions • processes of ingestion, digestion, absorption, assimilation and egestion • peristalsis • the role of digestive enzymes • bile – where produced and stored, and its role • structure of a villus helps absorption • *experiment to determine energy content in food*	8, 9, 10
f Respiration	• respiration releases energy • differences between aerobic and anaerobic respiration • equations for aerobic respiration • word equation for anaerobic respiration • *experiments on the evolution of carbon dioxide and heat from living organisms*	4
g Gas exchange	• the role of diffusion in gas exchange	7

Biology

Section	Content	Worksheets
g Gas exchange Flowering plants	• gas exchange in respiration and photosynthesis • **net exchange of carbon dioxide and oxygen depends on light** • leaf is adapted for gas exchange • role of stomata in gas exchange • *experiments on the effect of light on net gas exchange from a leaf*	21, 22, 25
g Gas exchange Humans	• structure of the thorax • ventilation • alveoli are adapted for gas exchange • biological consequences of smoking • *experiment to investigate the effect of exercise on breathing*	6, 7, 13
h Transport	• simple, unicellular organisms can rely on diffusion • need for a transport system in multicellular organisms	11
h Transport Flowering plants	• position of phloem and xylem in a stem • role of phloem • role of the xylem • how water is absorbed by root hair cells • transpiration is the evaporation of water • **rate of transpiration is affected by various factors** • *experiments that investigate the rate of transpiration*	25, 26
h Transport Humans	• composition of the blood • role of plasma in the transport of various substances • adaptations of red blood cells • role of white blood cells in preventing disease • platelets are involved in blood clotting • structure of the heart and how it functions • heart rate changes during exercise and due to adrenaline • structure of arteries, veins and capillaries and their roles • general plan of the circulation system	11, 12, 13
i Excretion Flowering plants	• origin of carbon dioxide and oxygen and their loss from stomata	21
i Excretion Humans	• lungs, kidneys and skin are organs of excretion • kidney in excretion and osmoregulation • structure of the urinary system • structure of a nephron • ultrafiltration and composition of the glomerular filtrate • water is reabsorbed from the collecting duct • **selective reabsorption of glucose occurs at the proximal convoluted tubule** • **role of ADH in regulating the water content of blood** • urine contains water, urea and salts	17
j Coordination and response	• organisms respond to changes • homeostasis and examples • coordinated response	14, 16, 18
j Coordination and response Flowering plants	• plants respond to stimuli • geotropic responses of roots and stems • phototropism of stems • **phototropic responses are caused by auxin** • *experiments to demonstrate phototropic and geotropic responses*	27

Biology

	Section	Content	Worksheets
j	**Coordination and response** Humans	• control of responses by nervous or by hormonal systems and differences between them • central nervous system • stimulation of receptors in sense organs sends impulses along nerves into and out of CNS • **structure and function of simple reflex arc** • structure and function of the eye as a receptor • function of eye in focusing, and response to changes in light intensity • **role of the skin in temperature regulation** • sources, roles and effects of: **ADH**, adrenaline, insulin, testosterone, progesterone and oestrogen	14, 15, 16, 17, 18, 20
3	**Reproduction and inheritance**		
a	**Reproduction**	• differences between sexual and asexual reproduction • fertilisation is fusion of male and female gametes to produce zygote	19, 28
a	**Reproduction** Flowering plants	• structures and adaptations of an insect-pollinated and a wind-pollinated flower • pollination and growth of pollen tube • fertilisation leads to seed and fruit formation • conditions needed for seed germination • germinating seeds utilise food reserves until photosynthesis • plants reproduce asexually by natural methods and by artificial methods	28, 29
a	**Reproduction** Humans	• structure and function of the male and female reproductive systems • roles of oestrogen and progesterone in menstrual cycle • fertilisation produces a zygote, cell division to form an embryo • role of the placenta • developing embryo protected by amniotic fluid • roles of oestrogen and testosterone in development of secondary sexual characteristics	19, 20
b	**Inheritance**	• nucleus contains chromosomes with genes • gene is a section of a molecule of DNA • genes exist as alleles • dominant, recessive, homozygous, heterozygous, phenotype, genotype and **codominance** • patterns of monohybrid inheritance and genetic diagrams • **interpret family pedigrees** • **predict probabilities of outcomes from monohybrid crosses** • sex of a person is controlled by one pair of chromosomes • determine sex of offspring using a genetic diagram • mitosis produces two cells with identical sets of chromosomes • occurs during growth, repair, cloning and asexual reproduction • meiosis produces four cells, each with half the number of chromosomes, results in formation of genetically different haploid gametes • random fertilisation produces genetic variation of offspring • diploid number in humans is 46 and the haploid number is 23	42, 43, 44, 45, 46, 47

Biology

	Section	Content	Worksheets
b	**Inheritance** (continued)	• variation within a species can be genetic, environmental, or combination • mutation is random change in genetic material that can be inherited • many mutations are harmful, some are neutral, a few are beneficial • mutant organisms can increase by natural selection • incidence of mutations can be increased by exposure to various factors	
4	**Ecology and the environment**		
a	**The organism in the environment**	• population, community, habitat and ecosystem • use of quadrats • *use of quadrats to estimate the population size in two different areas*	30
b	**Feeding relationships**	• producers, primary, secondary and tertiary consumers and decomposers • food chains, food webs, pyramids of number, pyramids of biomass, **pyramids of energy transfer** • transfer of substances and of energy along a food chain • **about 10% of energy is transferred from one trophic level to the next**	30, 31, 32, 33, 36
c	**Cycles within ecosystems**	• water cycle: evaporation, transpiration, condensation and precipitation • carbon cycle: respiration, photosynthesis, decomposition and combustion • **nitrogen cycle: nitrogen fixing bacteria, decomposers, nitrifying bacteria and denitrifying bacteria**	34, 35, 36
d	**Human influences on the environment**	• biological consequences of air pollution by sulphur dioxide and by carbon monoxide • water vapour, carbon dioxide, nitrous oxide, methane and CFCs are greenhouse gases • human activities contribute to greenhouse gases • increase in greenhouse gases and enhanced greenhouse effect, global warming and its consequences • biological consequences of pollution of water by sewage • **eutrophication due to fertiliser** • effects of deforestation • **biological consequences of overfishing and overgrazing**	37, 38, 39, 40, 41
5	**Use of biological resources**		
a	**Food production** Crop plants	• glasshouses and polythene tunnels used to increase crop yield • effects on crop yield of increased carbon dioxide and temperature • use of fertiliser to increase crop yield • pest control using pesticides and biological control	23, 33, 35, 37
a	**Food production** Microorganisms	• role of yeast in the production of beer • *carbon dioxide production by yeast in different conditions* • bacteria (*Lactobacillus*) in production of yoghurt • **industrial fermenters and suitable conditions for growth of microorganisms**	50
a	**Food production** Fish farming	• **methods used to farm large numbers of fish**	38

Biology

Section	Content	Worksheets
b Selective breeding	• plants and selective breeding • animals and selective breeding	48
c Genetic modification (genetic engineering)	• **DNA molecule is a double helix, the strands linked by paired bases** • **restriction enzymes cut DNA at specific sites and ligase enzymes join pieces of DNA** • **plasmids and viruses can act as vectors** • human insulin can be manufactured from genetically modified bacteria • using genetically modified plants to improve food production • **recall what the term transgenic means**	51, 52
d Cloning	• describe micropropagation (tissue culture) • micropropagation produces commercial quantities of identical plants (clones) • production of cloned mammals • **potential for using cloned transgenic animals**	49

Chemistry

Specification matching grid		
Section	**Content**	**Worksheets**
	Safety	1
I Principles of chemistry		
a Atoms	• smallness of particles and motion • define element and atom • relative atomic masses • **mole of atoms and Avogadro constant**	2, 13
b Atomic structure	• atom structure • relative mass and charge of particles • atomic number, mass number, isotopes and relative atomic mass (A_r) • **calculate relative atomic mass** • electronic configurations of first twenty elements • periodicity and electronic configuration • electronic configuration and chemical properties of Group 1 and Group 7 elements • importance of noble gas electronic configurations	2, 3, 14
c Relative formula masses and molar volumes	• calculate relative formula masses (M_r) • **mole as Avogadro constant number of particles or as relative formula mass** • **molar volumes of gases** • **significance of molar volume of a gas** • **use molar volume of a gas at stp and rtp**	15, 16
d Chemical formulae and chemical equations	• experiments to find formulae of simple compounds • formulae of compounds from experiments • **moles and finding chemical formulae** • **empirical formulae and molecular formulae** • **percentage yield and percentage purity** • determining relative numbers of particles involved in reactions • word equations • chemical equations that do not require balancing • use state symbols (l), (s), (g) and (aq) • **balanced chemical equations**	12, 13, 15, 16
e Ionic compounds	• formation of ions • electronic configuration and ionic charge • dot and cross model and formation of ionic compounds • ionic compounds have high mp and high bp • effect of increased ionic charge on mp and bp • **ionic bond is strong electrostatic attraction** • **ionic crystal is giant three-dimensional structure**	7, 10, 13
f Covalent substances	• covalent bonds share electron pairs and are strong • **covalent bond is attraction between bonding pair of electrons and nuclei** • dot and cross diagrams to represent single covalent bonds • **electron arrangement in some complex covalent molecules** • draw and describe the shapes of some molecules • simple molecular crystals • covalent molecular structures usually gases, liquids or solids with low mp and bp due to weak forces • physical properties of simple covalent compounds • diamond and graphite are allotropes of carbon • **giant molecular covalent structures of diamond and graphite and their use**	6, 9, 10

Chemistry

Section	Content	Worksheets
f Covalent substances (continued)	• **atoms in diamond and graphite are held by strong covalent bonds giving high sublimation points**	
g Electrolysis	• experiments to distinguish between electrolytes and non-electrolytes • electric current as a flow of electrons or ions • charges on common ions • **one Faraday is one mole of electrons** • **calculate amounts of products of electrolysis** • **write ionic half-equations for electrolysis** • oxidation as loss of electrons and reduction as gain of electrons • migration of ions provide evidence for ionic theory	32, 33, 34
h Metallic crystals	• **metal as a giant structure, electrons are free to move** • **structure of metal and physical properties**	8, 10, 17
2 Chemistry of the elements		
a The Periodic Table	• Periodic Table and atomic number • 'metals' and 'non-metals' and their properties • alkali metals (Group 1), the alkaline earth metals (Group 2) and the halogens (Group 7) • charges of ions and position in Periodic Table • relative reactivities in Groups 1, 2 and 7 • noble gases (Group 0) • **relationship between group number, number of outer electrons and metallic–nonmetallic character**	17, 38, 39
b Group 1 elements – lithium, sodium and potassium	• reactions with water • reactivities with water as basis for family of elements • simple physical and chemical properties of the hydroxides, halides, sulphates, nitrates and carbonates • **predict properties of other elements and compounds in group**	41
c Group 2 elements – magnesium and calcium	• reactions with water • simple physical and chemical properties of the oxides, hydroxides, chlorides, nitrates and carbonates • **predict properties of other elements and their compounds in group**	41
d Group 7 elements – chlorine, bromine and iodine	• colour and physical states at room temperature • interconversion of halogen and halide ion • hydrogen chloride and hydrochloric acid • properties of solutions of hydrogen chloride in water and in methylbenzene • laboratory preparation of chlorine • simple chemical test for chlorine • similarities in chemistry – family of elements • more reactive halogen will displace a less reactive halogen from a solution of one of its salts • **predict properties of other halogens**	42, 43
e Oxygen and oxides	• gases present in air and approximate percentage • industrial extraction of oxygen from air • reactions with oxygen in air of magnesium, iron, copper, carbon, sulphur and methane • determine percentage by volume of oxygen in air • oxidation and reduction as the addition and removal of oxygen • acidic nature of sulphur dioxide and reaction with water and alkalis • laboratory preparation of carbon dioxide	37, 45, 46

Chemistry

Section	Content	Worksheets
e Oxygen and oxides (continued)	• physical properties of carbon dioxide and reaction with water and alkalis • uses of carbon dioxide • reaction of nitrogen with oxygen to form nitrogen monoxide and nitrogen dioxide • conditions under which iron rusts • how rusting of iron and mild steel may be prevented • reduction of oxides in terms of reactivity	
f Sulphur and nitrogen	• physical characteristics of the allotropes of sulphur • reaction of sulphites with dilute acid • industrial extraction of nitrogen from air • importance of the inert nature of nitrogen • laboratory preparation of ammonia • physical properties of ammonia • simple chemistry of aqueous ammonia, ammonium chloride, ammonium nitrate and ammonium sulphate	46
g Hydrogen	• effect of dilute HCl and dilute H_2SO_4 on magnesium, aluminium, zinc and iron • laboratory preparation of hydrogen • combustion of hydrogen with oxygen • simple chemical test for water • physical test to show if water is pure • **reaction of hydrogen with chlorine**	20, 43, 45
h The transition metals - iron and copper	• action of steam, hydrogen chloride and chlorine on iron • formation of iron(II) and iron(III) hydroxides • redox reaction of concentrated nitric acid on copper • simple physical and chemical properties of copper(II) compounds • copper(I) compounds • **reaction of copper(II) ions with ammonia** • **transition metal properties**	20, 40, 44
i Reactivity series	• elements arranged in order of reactivity • pattern in the reactions of the elements and their compounds and reactivity series • reactions used to establish order of reactivity • reactivity series and displacement reactions • **sacrificial protection in terms of reactivity series**	18
j Preparing and analysing	• tests for cations • tests for anions • tests for gases • general rules for solubility in water • insoluble salts as precipitates • predict methods of preparing salts	47
3 Organic chemistry		
a Alkanes	• alkanes are saturated hydrocarbons • 'homologous series' and 'general formula' • shape of C bonds in alkanes • displayed formulae for alkanes • isomerism • **displayed formulae of alkanes** • **chlorination of methane**	49

Chemistry

	Section	Content	Worksheets
b	**Alkenes**	• alkenes are unsaturated hydrocarbons • shape of C bonds in alkenes • displayed formulae for alkenes • addition of halogens to alkenes • water as test for alkenes	49
c	**Ethanol**	• industrial preparation of ethanol • **factors relevant to method used in manufacture of ethanol** • **reaction of ethanol with sodium** • **oxidation of ethanol to ethanoic acid** • **dehydration of ethanol to ethene** • reaction of ethanol with carboxylic acids to form esters • esters and smell	52
4	**Physical chemistry**		
a	**States of matter**	• three states of matter • interconversion of gas, liquid and solid • differences between mixtures and compounds • techniques for separation • **states of matter and kinetic theory** • **heats of vaporisation for comparing energy needed**	4, 5, 11
b	**Acidity, alkalinity neutralisation**	• tests for acidity and alkalinity • colours produced by indicators • pH scale • pH of acidic, alkaline and neutral • acids and alkalis and proton transfer • prepare salts using neutralisation reactions • **acid–alkali titrations** • **calculations involving solutions in mol dm^{-3}** • **'weak' and 'strong' acids and alkalis**	19, 20, 21, 22, 23
c	**Energetics**	• chemical reactions and energy change • exothermic and endothermic reactions • energy changes • 'enthalpy change' • ΔH notation • principle of conservation of energy • **breaking of bonds is endothermic and making of bonds is exothermic** • **heats of reaction** • **draw energy profiles** • **use average bond dissociation energies**	24, 28, 29
d	**Rates of reaction**	• effect of surface area, concentration, temperature and the use of catalysts • experiments to investigate these effects • **explain effects of particle size, concentration and temperature using a simple kinetic model**	24, 25, 26, 27
e	**Equilibria**	• simple reversible reactions • **dynamic equilibrium and use of $\rightleftharpoons$** • **predict effects of changing conditions on reversible reactions**	31

Chemistry

Section	Content	Worksheets
5 Chemistry in Society		
a Extraction and uses of metals	• extraction of aluminium by electrolysis • **ionic half-equations for aluminium extraction** • reaction of carbon with metal oxides • extraction of iron in blast furnace • main reactions in extraction of iron • **extraction of zinc** • **extraction of chromium** • methods of extraction of metals related to reactivity series • purification of copper by electrolysis • important uses of metals	35, 36, 37
b Natural oil and gas	• crude oil is complex mixture of hydrocarbons • fractional distillation and crude oil • fractions obtained from crude oil • physical properties and uses of main fractions • incomplete combustion of fuels • carbon monoxide is poisonous • **fractional distillation produces more long-chain and fewer short-chain** • **cracking to give short-chain hydrocarbons** • **environmental damage by crude oil and hydrocarbons**	48, 50
c Synthetic polymers	• polymers formed from monomers • addition and condensation polymerisation • manufacture of poly(ethene) and structure • **principles of addition polymerisation** • uses of polymers and properties • recall the types of monomers used in the manufacture of the condensation polymer nylon • formation of nylon and structure • **principles of condensation polymerisation**	51
d The manufacture of some important chemicals	• manufacture of ammonia • conditions used in the Haber process • important uses of ammonia • **manufacture of nitric acid** • sources of sulphur • manufacture of sulphuric acid • important uses of sulphuric acid • sulphur dioxide and nitrogen oxides and acid rain • problems with acid rain • manufacture of sodium hydroxide and chlorine • important uses of sodium hydroxide and chlorine	30

Physics

Specification matching grid			
Section		**Content** **Worksheets**	
1 Forces and motion			
Units	1.1	use appropriate units	
Movement and position	1.2 1.3 1.4 1.5 1.6	distance–time graphs average speed, distance moved and time taken acceleration, velocity and time taken velocity–time graphs acceleration and distance travelled on velocity–time graphs	1, 2, 3
Forces, movement and shape	1.7 1.8 **1.9** **1.10** **1.11** 1.12 **1.13** 1.14 **1.15** 1.16 1.17 1.18 1.19 1.20 1.21 1.22	force as a push or pull types of force **vector and scalar quantities** **vector nature of a force** **add forces along a line** friction opposes motion **force = mass × acceleration** weight = mass × g **forces on falling objects and terminal velocity** factors affecting vehicle stopping distance relationship between moment of a force and distance from pivot weight and centre of gravity principle of moments for a simple system upward forces on beam vary with position of object extension and helical springs, metal wires and rubber bands force–extension graphs and Hooke's law	4, 5, 6, 7, 8, 9, 10
2 Electricity			
Units	2.1	use appropriate units	
Mains electricity	2.2 2.3 2.4 2.5 2.6 **2.7** 2.8	hazards of electricity insulation, double insulation, earthing, fuses and circuit breakers electrical heating in domestic contexts current in a resistor results in the electrical transfer of energy and an increase in temperature power = current × voltage and fuses **energy transferred = current × voltage × time** alternating current (a.c.) and direct current (d.c.)	11, 12, 13
Energy and potential difference in circuits	2.9 2.10 2.11 2.12 2.13 2.14 2.15 2.16 **2.17** **2.18**	series or parallel circuit for particular applications current in a series circuit depends on voltage and other components current varies with voltage changing resistance and current variation of resistance of LDRs and thermistors voltage = current × resistance current is rate of flow of charge charge = current × time **electric current is flow of negatively charged** **electrons** **voltage is energy transferred per unit charge passed/** **joule per coulomb**	16, 17, 18, 19, 20

Physics

Section	Content	Worksheets
Electric charge	2.19 electrical conductors and insulators 2.20 charging insulating materials by friction 2.21 electrostatic charges produced by loss and gain of electrons 2.22 forces of attraction and repulsion 2.23 electrostatic phenomena and movement of electrons 2.24 potential dangers of electrostatic charges 2.25 uses of electrostatic charges	14, 15
3 Waves		
Units	3.1 use appropriate units	
Properties of waves	3.2 longitudinal and transverse waves in ropes, springs and water 3.3 amplitude, frequency, wavelength and period of a wave 3.4 waves transfer energy and information without transferring matter 3.5 wave speed = frequency × wavelength 3.6 frequency = 1/time period 3.7 use above relationships in different contexts 3.8 waves can be diffracted and extent of diffraction depends on wavelength and size of gap	21, 22
The electromagnetic spectrum	3.9 electromagnetic spectrum and speed of waves 3.10 order of electromagnetic spectrum in decreasing wavelength and increasing frequency 3.11 uses of electromagnetic radiations 3.12 detrimental effects of excessive exposure of the human body to electromagnetic waves	23, 24
Light and sound	3.13 light waves are transverse waves, can be reflected, refracted and diffracted 3.14 angle of incidence equals the angle of reflection 3.15 ray diagrams and formation of a virtual image in a plane mirror 3.16 investigate refraction of light 3.17 $n = \sin i / \sin r$ **3.18 determine refractive index of glass** 3.19 total internal reflection in transmitting information **3.20 critical angle c** **3.21 $\sin c = 1/n$** 3.22 difference between analogue and digital signals 3.23 sound waves are longitudinal waves, can be reflected, refracted and diffracted 3.24 frequency range of human hearing 3.25 measure speed of sound in air **3.26 oscilloscope and microphone can display sound waves** **3.27 determine frequency of a sound wave** **3.28 pitch depends on frequency of vibration of source** **3.29 loudness depends on amplitude of vibration**	25, 26, 27, 28
4 Energy resources and energy transfer		
Units	4.1 use appropriate units	
Energy transfer	4.2 describe energy transfers 4.3 energy is conserved 4.4 efficiency = useful energy output / total energy output 4.5 everyday and scientific devices and situations and fate of input energy including use of flow diagrams 4.6 conduction, convection and radiation 4.7 role of convection in everyday phenomena 4.8 insulation used to reduce energy transfers	29, 30, 31, 32, 33, 34

Physics

Section	Content	Worksheets

Work and power	4.9 work done = force × distance moved
	4.10 work done is equal to energy transferred
	**4.11 gravitational potential energy = mass × g × height
	        kinetic energy = 1/2 × mass × speed²**
	**4.12 conservation of energy links potential energy,
	        kinetic energy and work**
	4.13 power as rate of transfer of energy or rate of doing work
	4.14 power = work done / time taken
		35

Energy resources and electricity generation	4.15 energy transfers in generating electricity **4.16 advantages and disadvantages of electricity production from various resources**	36, 37
5 Solids, liquids and gases		
Units	5.1 use appropriate units	
Density and pressure	5.2 density = mass / volume 5.3 determine density using direct measurements of mass and volume 5.4 pressure = force / area 5.5 pressure at a point in a gas or liquid 5.6 pressure difference = height × density × g	38

Change of state	5.7 change state from solid to liquid by melting
	5.8 change state from liquid to gas by evaporation or boiling
	5.9 particles in liquid have random motion within a
	      close-packed structure
	5.10 particles in a solid vibrate about fixed positions within a
	        close-packed regular structure
		39

Ideal gas molecules	5.11 Brownian motion
	5.12 molecules in a gas have random motion and exert a force
	        and pressure
	5.13 absolute zero of temperature, −273 °C
	5.14 kelvin scale of temperature and convert between the kelvin
	        and Celsius scales
	5.15 increase in temperature and increase in speed of gas
	        molecules
	**5.16 kelvin temperature proportional to average kinetic
	        energy of molecules**
	5.17 qualitative relationship between pressure and kelvin
	        temperature
	5.18 $p_1 / T_1 = p_2 / T_2$
	5.19 $p_1 V_1 = p_2 V_2$
		39

6 Magnetism and electromagnetism		
Units	6.1 use appropriate units	

Magnetism	6.2 magnets repel and attract other magnets, and attract
	      magnetic substances
	6.3 properties of magnetically hard and soft materials
	6.4 magnetic field lines
	6.5 magnetism induced when some materials are placed in a
	      magnetic field
	6.6 magnetic field patterns
	6.7 use two permanent magnets to produce uniform magnetic
	      field pattern
		40

Physics

Section	Content	Worksheets
Electromagnetism	6.8 electric current produces magnetic field 6.9 construction of electromagnets 6.10 magnetic field patterns for straight wire, flat circular coil and solenoid 6.11 force on a charged particle moving in a magnetic field 6.12 force exerted on current-carrying wire in a magnetic field, and simple d.c. electric motors and loudspeakers **6.13 direction of resulting force when wire carries current perpendicular to a magnetic field** **6.14 force on a current-carrying conductor in magnetic field and strength of field and current**	40, 41
Electromagnetic induction	6.15 voltage induced when conductor moves through magnetic field or magnetic field changes, and factors which affect size of induced voltage 6.16 generation of electricity and factors which affect size of induced voltage 6.17 structure of transformer and effect of different numbers of turns on input and output sides 6.18 use of step-up and step-down transformers 6.19 input (primary)voltage / output (secondary) voltage = primary turns / secondary turns **6.20 input power = output power for 100% efficiency**	42, 43
7 Radioactivity and particles		
Units	7.1 use appropriate units	
Radioactivity	7.2 structure of an atom and use symbols to describe nuclei 7.3 atomic (proton) number, mass (nucleon) number and isotope 7.4 emission of alpha and beta particles and gamma rays 7.5 nature of alpha and beta particles and gamma rays and penetrating power **7.6 atomic and mass numbers and emission of radiation** **7.7 complete balanced nuclear equations** 7.8 detection of ionising radiations by photographic film or GM detector 7.9 sources of background radiation 7.10 activity decreases over time, measured in becquerels 7.11 'half-life', different for different isotopes 7.12 use the half-life in simple calculations 7.13 uses of radioactivity 7.14 dangers of ionising radiations	44, 45, 46, 47, 48
Particles	**7.15 Geiger and Marsden's experiments** **7.16 Rutherford's nuclear model and Geiger and Marsden's experiment** **7.17 fission of U-235, and how releases energy** **7.18 products of fission of U-235** **7.19 chain reaction in U-235 nuclei** **7.20 control rods and moderator in fission process**	49

Biology answers

1 This is your life

1 Seven, respiration, excrete, move, reproduce, sensitivity
2 Concrete, no ticks; car, ticks for needs food (petrol), respires using oxygen (at least needs oxygen), excretes (exhaust), moves; pig, tick everything.
3 a X = cell membrane, Y = nucleus, Z = cytoplasm
   b X controls the movement of chemicals in and out of the cell. Y controls the activities of the cell. Z where most of the chemical reactions of the cell take place.
   c i Cell A, epithelial cell/glandular epithelial cell;
      ii cell B, muscle cell
   d i Tissue A lines the surface of the stomach/ produces useful substances, e.g. enzymes, mucus.
      ii Tissue B contracts making the stomach wall move and change shape.
   e Digestive system.
4 Cell A, nerve cell; long axon for carrying electrical messages distances around the body, lots of dendrites to link with other nerve cells.
   Cell B, fat cell; simple shapes very little cytoplasm, both of these things make it possible for the cell to store as much fat as possible.

2 Maintaining life

1 Reproduce/excrete, excrete/reproduce (alternative to the answer given before), movement, slow, sensitivity

2

Organ	What it does
heart	pumps blood around the lungs and/or the body
stomach	mixes the food with acid / starts to digest the protein/food
brain	co-ordinates all the messages from the sense organs and sends out messages to the body
eye	picks up light from the world around us and sends messages back into the brain (lets us see – allow or not depending on the ability of the class)

3 a To capture sunlight energy/to make food (by photosynthesis could gain extra credit).
   b To support the leaves and flowers and transport substances around the plant.
   c To anchor the plant in the soil and get water and mineral ions from the soil.
   d Reproduction of the plant/to make seeds.
4 a Respiration
   b From their food
   c They make food from carbon dioxide and water using energy from the Sun in a process known as photosynthesis.

   d Animals have to eat other organisms to get food. They either eat plants directly, or eat animals which have eaten plants.
5 a Because our cells are still working and growing, and muscles in our heart and breathing system are still working.
   b Because we continue to need new cells to replace old ones and to repair damaged ones.

3 Speeding things up

1 a A catalyst will speed up or slow down a reaction but is not changed itself.
   b Living organisms make very efficient catalysts known as enzymes.
   c All enzymes are made of protein.
   d The reactions that take place in your cells wouldn't happen fast enough to keep you alive without enzymes.
   e Digestive enzymes break down large food molecules into smaller ones.
   f Each type of enzyme breaks down a specific type of molecule.
2 a 2.0   b 7.0
   c Kills off most of the bacteria in food.
3 a Amylase breaks down starch. Evidence: iodine no longer turns black to indicate the presence of starch.
   b Increase in temperature increases the speed of the reaction.
   c As a control, to make sure that starch wouldn't break down anyway.
   d It wouldn't work as well, may stop working completely, because pH affects enzyme activity.

4 Releasing energy

1 Fuels, heat, food, energy, glucose
2 a Energy is released from glucose by a process called respiration.
   b During respiration chemical reactions take place inside the cells of your body.
   c When glucose reacts with oxygen energy is released.
   d In respiration, carbon dioxide and water are formed as waste products.
   e Because it uses oxygen from the air the process is known as aerobic respiration.
3 Making new molecules to help you grow and repair your body, for moving around, and to keep you warm.
4 a Oxygen, glucose, energy, respiration, carbon dioxide, water
   b Oxygen + glucose → water + carbon dioxide + energy
5 a Glucose → lactic acid + energy
   b It allows you to keep exercising when there is not enough oxygen to produce all the energy you need aerobically.

c The lactic acid builds up while you exercise anaerobically and has to be broken down afterwards.

d You need oxygen to break down the lactic acid.

6 a The purple colour spread out from the crystal through the water.

b i Diffusion

ii The net movement of particles from an area of high concentration to an area of low concentration along a concentration gradient. Movement is as a result of the kinetic energy of the particles.

c The purple colour would spread more rapidly through the water in beaker B than beaker A.

d The rate of diffusion of a substance is greater at higher temperatures. The higher temperature gives the diffusing particles more kinetic energy. They will move around faster, increasing the movement along a concentration gradient and – in this case – making the purple particles spread faster through the water.

5 The variety of life

1 a i multicellular
ii cells contain chloroplasts
iii no chloroplasts
iv cells have cellulose cell walls
v cells can change shape
vi carry out photosynthesis
vii feed on other organisms
viii glycogen
ix don't move whole organism around
x move whole body in coordinated way

b Vertebrates have backbones/vertebral column, invertebrates lack a vertebral column.

2 a Any sensible answer e.g. yeast, mushroom, mould etc.

b They don't contain chlorophyll so they cannot photosynthesise. They contain chitin in their cells walls, not cellulose.

c i Thread-like filaments that make up the main body of a fungus like a mushroom underground.
ii The whole network of hyphae.
iii The reproductive cell of a fungus.

3 a As page 17 of Student's book.
b As page 18 of Student's book.
c i The hyphae secrete digestive enzymes onto the food. The enzymes break the food down into soluble molecules such as sugars which are then absorbed by the mould. They are known as extracellular enzymes.
ii Saprotrophic nutrition

4 A cell wall, B chromosome, C flagellum, D plasmids, E capsule, F DNA or RNA, G envelope (membrane from host cell), H protein coat

5 a Bacteria are much bigger (c. 5 μm) than viruses (0.01–0.1 μm).

b Viruses only reproduce and do this parasitically, bacteria carry out all the normal processes of living organisms – feed, respire, grow, excrete, move, respond and reproduce.

c Bacteria carry out many useful functions: in the gut, as decomposers, in food production etc, some cause disease and food decay. All naturally occurring viruses cause disease but they can now be made and used in genetic engineering.

6 The breath of life

1 Breathing system, lungs, carbon dioxide, diaphragm, alveoli

2 alveoli, millions of tiny air sacs making up the gas exchange tissue; trachea, the main air passage leading in from the mouth and nose; lungs, the body organs where gas exchange takes place; diaphragm, large sheet of muscle separating the thorax from the abdomen; bronchioles, the smallest air passages in the lungs; thorax, the upper part of the body containing the lungs.

3 a Ribs lifted up and outwards (by muscles between ribs); diaphragm muscle contracts, pulling diaphragm down and flat; increases the volume of the chest so the pressure falls; air rushes into the lungs to equalise the pressure.

b Ribs move down and inwards as muscles relax; diaphragm relaxes and domes upwards again; volume of chest gets smaller so pressure gets greater; air squeezed out of the lungs.

4 a Correctly plotted bar chart.

b Person B fittest, lowest breathing rate at rest and least affected by exercise. Person A least fit, highest resting breathing rate and most affected by exercise.

c It gets deeper.

d Our tissues need more oxygen as they are respiring more to provide more energy as the muscles are working. The breathing rate and depth increase to supply the extra oxygen and get rid of the extra carbon dioxide formed in respiration.

5 A: As the race gets going breathing rate increases to supply the muscles with the extra oxygen they need to get the energy required for the muscles to work using aerobic respiration. B: The breathing rate plateaus at its maximum, the body cannot get any more air (or oxygen) in. If there is not enough oxygen for the needs of the muscles some anaerobic respiration will take place and lactic acid will build up. C: Although the exercise is finished the breathing rate remains raised, gradually returning to normal as the oxygen debt is paid off. D: Breathing has returned to the normal resting rate.

7 Exchanging gases

1 A, In the cells of your body, respiration …
B, In your lungs, you exchange …
C, You breathe in, …
D, Your circulatory system …

2 Oxygen is taken from the air in the lungs into the blood, so the concentration of oxygen in the air breathed out is lower than the concentration in the air breathed in. In the lungs carbon dioxide moves from the blood into the air, so the air breathed out contains more carbon dioxide than the air breathed in. This is known as gas exchange.

3 a A, thin-walled capillary; B, carbon dioxide diffuses out; C, air in; D, air out; E, thin membrane of alveolus; F oxygen diffuses in.
  b Thin walls of capillary and alveolus make short distance for gases to diffuse; rich blood supply maintains concentration gradient which makes diffusion in both directions more efficient; large surface area for diffusion to take place over.

4 a Tar, nicotine, carbon monoxide
  b Any three from: destroys cilia lining breathing tubes allowing mucus build-up and encouraging infection; breaks down walls of alveoli; causes lung cancer; carbon monoxide reduces oxygen concentration in blood causing heart disease and reducing growth rate of an unborn fetus; increases fatty plaques in blood vessels leading to thrombosis, stroke and heart disease.

5 a i 8100 cm³ ii 15 000 cm³
    iii 43 050 cm³
  b Bar chart correctly drawn.
  c Because when you exercise your muscles use more energy. They get the energy from food in the process of respiration, and for respiration you need oxygen. As you exercise you need more oxygen and so you need to breathe more often and more deeply to get more air to provide more oxygen.
  d The blood flow through the heart gets greater, more blood is pumped with each heart beat and there are more beats per minute. This extra blood flow is needed to carry more food and oxygen to the muscle cells for respiration.

8 Healthy eating

1 Healthy, energy, chemicals, carbohydrates/fats, fats/carbohydrates, malnutrition

2 a Carbohydrates are found in foods such as cereals, fruits and root vegetables.
  b Both carbohydrates and fats supply energy but the energy in the carbohydrates can be used more easily by the body.
  c Fats are found in foods such as cheese, butter and margarine.
  d Too much, too little or the wrong sort of food causes malnutrition.
  e Proteins, important for growth and replacing cells, are found in meat, fish, eggs and pulses.

3

Carbohydrates	Proteins	Fats
crispy rice cereal	skimmed milk	cream
sugar	bread (roll)	chicken
bread (roll)	bun	chips
bun	cream	pastry of apple
apple	apple	pie
chips	chicken	crisps
sweetcorn	chips	
peas	sweetcorn	
apple pie	peas	
lemonade	apple pie	
chewing gum		
orange		

4 a Different lifestyles, different research, different government aims, or any other reasonable answer.
  b Because individuals vary, so one value isn't right for everybody.
  c More confusing because of the adding up to 100% for an individual, but more applicable to a population.

9 Cutting food down to size

1 Digested, digestive system, mouth, gut, enzymes, bloodstream

2 a A stomach   B large intestine
    C small intestine D anus
    E pancreas   F mouth
    G oesophagus (gullet) H liver
  b Stomach, secretes hydrochloric acid and protease, churns food to aid mechanical digestion. Large intestine, mainly absorbtion of water from digested food. Small intestine, digestion of many food types and absorbtion of digested food into the body. Anus, where undigested food is expelled from the body. Pancreas, secretes several enzymes for digesting food. Mouth, where food is taken into the body. Oesophagus, connects the mouth to the stomach. Liver, produces bile which aids digestion of lipids.

3 a protein   b amino acids
  c carbohydrate   d lipase   e fatty acids

4 a USA and Japan
  b Correctly drawn bar chart.
  c Uganda (7.5 per 100 000) and India (7.6 per 100 000)
  d USA (44.4 per 100 000) and England and Wales (33.9 per 100 000)
  e Mostly – the link with low incidence and high fibre is clearer than a link between high incidence and low fibre.
  f You would need to correlate with many other factors that could possibly affect the development of bowel cancer, such as level of activity, and then see which factors showed the clearest links.

10 Getting food into the body

1 Soluble, digested, gut, dissolve, blood
2 a Gut muscles squeezing food through the gut.
   b A layers of muscle in the wall of the intestine
     B muscles contract to squeeze food along
     C direction the food is pushed in

3 Large surface area greatly increases the surface area of the gut for dissolved food to pass through; rich blood supply to carry away the absorbed food (maintaining a concentration gradient); very thin walls so short diffusion distances, food can easily pass into the blood.

4 Gut A: Starch did not break down, cannot pass through the model gut by diffusion. Therefore in the water surrounding the model there was no starch and no glucose. Gut B: At room temperature amylase breaks starch down to glucose slowly. As the glucose is formed it can pass out of the gut by diffusion and so appears in the water, giving a positive Benedict's test. Gut C: At body temperature the enzyme works faster and so glucose appears in the water surrounding the model gut much quicker.

11 Blood – supplying your body's needs

1 Transported, blood, glucose, oxygen, waste products, circulatory, heart
2 a Plasma
   b These cells have no nucleus. They are packed with the red pigment haemoglobin which carries oxygen.
   c These cells have a nucleus and help defend the body against microorganisms which cause disease.
   d Platelets

3

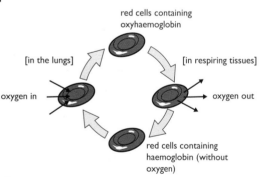

red cells containing
oxyhaemoglobin

[in the lungs]   [in respiring tissues]

oxygen in   oxygen out

red cells containing
haemoglobin (without
oxygen)

4 a People living at high altitude develop a high red blood cell count because they need more red blood cells to be able to get enough oxygen from the air. Without the extra cells they would be breathless as soon as they tried to do anything and might collapse, as often happens when people who live at low altitudes visit very high regions.
   b The athlete will have a high red cell count because they will have more blood than normal. This means that their blood can carry more oxygen than normal, and so gives them an advantage during the race.

   c Iron is needed to make haemoglobin, the red pigment in red blood cells. If a person is anaemic their body will not be able to make as much haemoglobin as normal and so will not be able to make as many red blood cells either. They will feel tired and lacking in energy because their cells will be short of oxygen needed for cellular respiration.

12 On the beat

1 Blood vessels, circulatory system, heart, pumps, capillaries.
2 a Blood enters the heart through the atria.
   b The atria contract and force blood into the ventricles.
   c The ventricles contract and force blood out of the heart.
   d The blood leaving the right side of the heart is pumped to the lungs.
   e The blood leaving the left side of the heart is pumped around the body.
3 a Red on right *as you look at the page*, blue on left *as you look at the page* and merging colours in the capillary areas.
   b Oxygen and carbon dioxide exchanged with alveoli, so blood leaving lungs has higher concentration of oxygen and lower concentration of carbon dioxide.
   c Oxygen and carbon dioxide exchanged with body cells, so blood leaving the cells has higher concentration of carbon dioxide and lower concentration of oxygen.
   d Because the blood is circulated round the lungs, returns to the heart and is then circulated around the body, so there are two separate circulation systems.
4 a A artery   B vein   C capillary
   b Arteries have a pulse. They carry blood away from the heart, usually oxygenated blood. Capillaries carry blood to the individual cells of the body and it is here that substances diffuse into and out of the blood. Veins carry blood towards the heart, usually deoxygenated blood.

5 a If there is a hole in the heart then oxygenated and deoxygenated blood is no longer kept separate. It can mix, and the level of oxygen in the blood going round the body is not as high as it should be. This explains the blue colour and the lack of energy. If surgeons close up the hole, the heart works perfectly normally and the blood no longer mixes.
   b The heart muscle itself is starved of oxygen and so cannot work properly. This is why the chest pain develops. If the damaged blood vessels are replaced with healthy ones then the blood flow to the heart muscle is restored, it is no longer starved of oxygen and can work properly again.

13 Fit for life

1 Fit, healthy, exercise, heart/circulation, circulation/heart.

2 A, C, E

3 **a** Bar charts correctly drawn.

    b **i** Has a greater volume and pumps more blood at each beat. Beats more slowly at rest.

        ii Lowers the breathing rate.

4 **a** Correctly plotted graph.

    b Muscles need increased levels of oxygen and food for aerobic respiration to provide the energy needed for the contraction of the muscles. The heart beats faster and with a bigger volume to increase the blood supply to the muscles, which in turn delivers the food and oxygen needed. It also removes the extra carbon dioxide produced. Once the exercise is over, the heart rate can return to normal.

    c Control of the heart rate relies on nerve impulses from the medulla. Carbon dioxide concentration in the blood rises when we exercise as a result of more cellular respiration. Sensors in the aorta and carotid arteries detect the change and send nerve impulses to the medulla. The medulla responds by sending impulses along the accelerator nerve which stimulates the heart to beat faster and more strongly. When the exercise is over and carbon dioxide concentration drops, the medulla receives fewer impulses. In response, it sends nerve impulses to the decelerator nerve which in turn decreases the heart rate and makes it contract with less force.

14 Responding to change

1 **a** light   **b** sound   **c** ears

    d chemicals, enable us to taste   **e** nose

    f pressure and temperature changes

2 Nervous system, stimulus, senses, receptors, coordinates, controls.

3 **a** Detect changes in the environment/stimuli, e.g. eyes respond to light, ears to sound.

    b Receives information from all the sensory organs, makes sense of the information and controls the responses of various parts of our bodies. It also provides us with an image of the world around us.

    c Carry impulses from the sense organs to the central nervous system.

    d Carry impulses from the central nervous system to the muscles.

4 **a** Voluntary action involves conscious thought and control by the sensory nervous system, but a reflex action does not.

    b They allow important repetitive actions (e.g. breathing, control of the heart, gut) to take place without using up conscious thought and they allow a very rapid response to danger or pain, faster than if conscious centres are involved.

    c **i** blow below kneecap → receptor in skin/tendon → spinal cord → muscles of leg → knee jerks

        ii pain from sharp point → receptor in skin → spinal cord → muscles of leg → foot withdrawn

        iii sound /movement → eyes/ears → brain → muscles of eyelids → blink

5 **a** Answers along the lines of:

    1 receptors in the skin detect stimulus

    2 impulses pass along sensory neurones to spinal cord

    3 relay neurones in spinal cord transfer impulses from sensory neurones to motor neurones

    4 impulses pass from spinal cord along motor neurones to reach muscles

    5 impulses cause muscles to contract, hand is pulled away without conscious thought.

    b Impulses also pass to the brain from the hand and muscles and, combined with impulses from the eyes seeing what is happening, you have a conscious realisation of the hot plate and the reflex action a very short time after it has happened.

15 The way of seeing

1 **a** retina   **b** sclera   **c** iris

    d cornea   **e** lens   **f** optic nerve

    g pupil   **h** ciliary muscles

    i suspensory ligaments

2

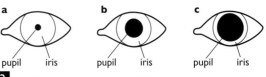

    a pupil iris   **b** pupil iris   **c** pupil iris

3 **a** If the cornea is cloudy, light cannot get through into the eye, making it impossible to see. Able pupils may comment that the blindness will be progressive as the cornea becomes increasingly cloudy.

    b The cornea and lens focus light on the retina. If the eyeball is an unusual shape, light from distant objects will tend to be focused in front of the retina so lenses are needed to bend the light from distant objects before it enters the eye.

    c The retina contains light-sensitive cells. If the retina becomes detached there are no working sensory cells to detect light and it will be impossible to see.

4 **a** Ciliary muscles change shape of lens to make it thicker, bends light more, bringing it into focus on retina.

    b Ciliary muscles change shape of lens making it thinner, bends light less, bringing it into focus on retina.

    c The headset made the objects they were seeing upside down, so the image on the retina was actually right way up, leading the brain to interpret it as upside down. After a few days the brain learnt this and stopped interpreting the image as upside down, so that the people saw the world normally again. Then when the headsets were removed, it took a while for the brain to re-learn the normal interpretation of visual information, so the image was perceived as upside down.

16 Staying in control
1 Nervous, electrical, rapid, chemical, glands, blood, long-term
2 Hormone, a chemical message carried in the blood which causes a change in the body; insulin, a hormone made in the pancreas which causes sugar to pass from the blood into cells where it is needed for energy; diabetes, a condition when the pancreas cannot make enough insulin to control the blood sugar.
3 **a** and **b** Any five from:
- Breathing rate increases and breaths deeper – takes more oxygen into the body for more respiration to release more energy.
- Heart beats faster – more blood gets to muscles faster to deliver more oxygen and glucose for respiration.
- Blood diverted away from intestines – so more blood available to go to muscles.
- Stored carbohydrate in liver changed into glucose and released into blood – so more glucose available for respiration in muscle cells.
- Pupils in eyes dilate – so more sensitive to detecting movement.
- Body hair stands on end – makes animal look larger to enemy.
- Mental awareness increased – so reactions are faster.

4

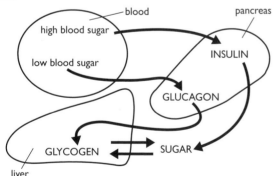

liver

5 **a** Blood sugar concentration goes up after a meal, so the pancreas releases insulin which allows the sugar to go into the cells and the blood sugar concentration to drop.
b The concentration of sugar in the blood keeps on rising because no insulin is produced, so the sugar cannot get into the cells and the concentration in the blood gets higher and higher.
c Insulin injections mean that sugar can get into the cells to provide them with energy and blood sugar concentration does not get dangerously high.

The pattern is quite similar to that of a person with a healthy pancreas.

17 Cleaning the bloodstream
1 Waste products, respiration, lungs, amino acids, urea, kidneys, urine
2 **a** As moisture in air we breathe out, as sweat.
  b In our sweat.
  c None, because they are reabsorbed in the kidneys.
3

Substance	point A	point B
glucose	filtered from blood into capsule	actively taken back into the blood
dissolved minerals	filtered from blood into capsule	minerals needed by the body are absorbed back into the blood
urea	filtered into blood from capsule	most remains in the tubule

4 **a** The volume of urine rose well over the normal level to a peak about 90 minutes after drinking the water. The volume of urine produced then gradually reduced until by 150 minutes it was almost back to normal level.
b Drinking water makes the blood more dilute. This stops the production of the hormone ADH. ADH makes the tubule walls more permeable, so when it is not released the walls of the tubule are less permeable and so less water is absorbed back into the blood. As a result more urine is formed and the blood concentration is returned to normal.
c As the volume of urine increased, the salt concentration decreased.
d The change in salt concentration is because the amount of salt being lost in the urine remains the same, but because there is a lot more water in the urine the salt is more diluted and so the concentration falls.
e Would expect the volume of urine produced to fall below the normal level and to continue to fall until another drink was taken. As the volume of the urine falls the salt concentration of the urine would increase, with the same amount of salt dissolved in smaller volumes of water.

18 Keeping warm and staying cool
1 Constant, enzymes, die, sweating.
2 **a** D, A, C, B
  b She would need to drink more to replace the liquid she lost through sweating.
3 **a** Person 37 °C, frog 18 °C
  b About 10 °C, because reactions slow down, hypothermia develops and heart beat and breathing will stop.

c About 55 °C, because once the body temperature goes over 40 °C enzymes start to denature and do not work properly.

d Shiver to produce heat, goosepimples as try to trap layer of air next to skin, blood supply to skin and extremities reduced to keep warmth deep in core, plus behavioural changes, e.g. move about, put more clothes on, turn on heating.

e Sweat to lose heat by evaporation, blood vessels dilate allowing lots of blood to flow near surface of skin and so increase heat loss, also behavioural changes, e.g. remove clothing, find cool shady place.

4 Poster should be clear and carry message in a clear and positive way.

19 Human reproduction

1 a The new individual formed in asexual reproduction is identical to the parent.

b In sexual reproduction special male and female sex cells fuse (join) to form a unique new cell.

c The new individual formed in sexual reproduction contains a mixture of genetic information from both parents.

d The special sex cells involved in sexual reproduction are known as gametes.

e A clone is the identical offspring formed as a result of asexual reproduction.

2 a Follicle stimulating hormone (FSH), luteinising hormone (LH) and testosterone.

b Follicle stimulating hormone (FSH), luteinising hormone (LH) and oestrogen.

c

In boys	In girls
sperm production starts	menstrual cycle begins, and eggs are released by the ovaries every month
growth and development of male sexual organs	growth and development of female sexual organs
growth of armpit hair and pubic hair, and chest and facial hair (beard)	growth of armpit hair and pubic hair
increase in body mass	increase in body mass
growth of muscles	development of 'rounded' shape to hips
voice breaks	voice deepens without sudden 'breaking'
sexual 'drive' develops	sexual 'drive' develops
	breasts develop

3 a A ovary, B Fallopian tube (oviduct), C uterus (womb), D cervix, E vagina

b A testis, B penis, C erectile tissue, D sperm duct, E seminal vesicle

c i Semen containing sperm is ejaculated from the penis into the vagina during sexual intercourse. The sperm swim towards the Fallopian tubes. An egg is released from the ovary at ovulation and travels along one of the Fallopian tube. The sperm meet the egg and one of them penetrates the egg. Fertilisation takes place as they fuse together.

ii The placenta provides the fetus with oxygen and food from the mother's blood, and allows the fetus to get rid of waste products such as carbon dioxide and urea. It also anchors the fetus to the uterus wall. (Extra marks can be awarded for a suitable diagram.)

iii In the first stage, the cervix dilates to allow the baby through as the result of the contraction of the muscles of the uterus. In the second stage, the baby is delivered as strong contractions of the uterus push the baby, usually head first, though the cervix and the vagina to the outside world. Finally the uterus expels the placenta and the membranes which have surrounded the baby as it developed.

20 The menstrual cycle

1 Ovaries, uterus, hormone, blood.

2 Pituitary gland, small gland in the brain which produces hormones which control fertility by affecting the ovary.

Ovary, releases a ripe egg each month and makes the hormones oestrogen and progesterone which control the menstrual cycle.

Uterus (womb), where the fetus develops for 9 months; if no pregnancy occurs, the blood-rich lining is shed each month.

Oviduct, the site where fertilisation of the egg by the sperm takes place.

Vagina, where sperm from a man's penis enter the body during sexual intercourse.

3

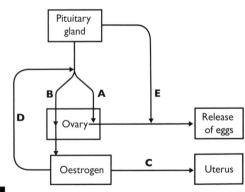

4 a If too much is given there is a risk of multiple ovulation, and of several babies starting to develop in the uterus at the same time.

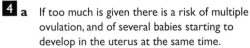

b i So lots of ripe eggs are produced at one time. This helps to make sure there are enough eggs for at least one to be fertilised successfully and, as spare embryos can be frozen, may mean the harvesting of the eggs will not have to be repeated.

   ii To make sure the lining of the uterus builds up ready to support a pregnancy.

21 The energy factory

1 Photosynthesis, light, chlorophyll, chloroplasts, water, sugar (glucose), starch.

2 a Carbon dioxide gas is absorbed from the air.
   Water from the root moves up to the leaf through the stem.
   Sunlight provides energy.
   Sugars are made in the leaf and provide the plant with food.
   Oxygen is produced and released into the air.

b Carbon dioxide + water $\xrightarrow{\text{energy from the Sun}}$ sugar + water

3

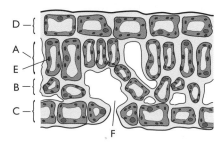

4 a Starch

b The mass of the potato crop depended on the amount of sunlight in the growing season. Most of the mass of a potato is made of starch, and starch is made as a direct result of photosynthesis. The amount of photosynthesis which can take place depends on the amount of sunlight available to supply the energy, so the amount of sunlight is directly linked to the size of the potato crop.

5 a i starch   **ii** cell walls
   iii cytoplasm, enzymes

b To release energy in respiration.

22 Plant design

1 Leaves use energy from light to make food.
   Stems hold the plant upright and transport substances between other parts.
   Roots anchor the plant firmly in the ground.
   Flowers where sexual reproduction takes place.

2

3 a

b Palisade layer, cells contain many chloroplasts, where most photosynthesis takes place. Spongy layer, main gas exchange surface in leaf. Lower epidermis, protect cells inside leaf, where most stomata are found. Upper epidermis, protect cells inside leaf. Chloroplast, where light energy used to make glucose from water and carbon dioxide. Stomata, small hole that allows gases into and out of leaf.

23 Bigger and better crops

1 Photosynthesis, carbon dioxide, oxygen, light, temperature, limit.

2 a Bubbles of gas formed from plant.

b i More bubbles/it would bubble faster.
   ii Fewer bubbles/it would bubble slower.

c Because plants need light for photosynthesis. If they have more light they can usually photosynthesise faster, but if they have less light they will photosynthesise slower.

d The temperature might be changing because the light gets hot.

3 a Correctly plotted graph with labelled lines for 85% and 35% on the same axes.

b Seedlings in 85% sunlight receive more light energy than those in 35% sunlight. This means they can carry out more photosynthesis and use the sugars they make to build more new tissue. The seedlings grown in higher light levels grow taller than those grown in less light.

4 a 25–30 °C

b Causes a steady increase in the rate of photosynthesis up to around 30 °C after which the rate starts to fall.

c 50 °C

d In respiration the plant uses the food it makes in photosynthesis. When the difference between respiration and photosynthesis is greatest, the largest amount of sugar will be available to turn into tomato.

e 28 °C

24 How does your garden grow?

I Cuttings, propagator, humid, light, nitrates.

2 a To make proteins from the sugars made during photosynthesis.

b From the soil through their roots (most able may remember active transport).

c From decaying bodies of animals and plants or from fertilisers.

d The fertiliser makes the algae grow rapidly, but they block out the light killing other water plants. As the algae die they are decomposed by bacteria and this uses up lots of oxygen out of the water, so that fish and other animals die. This leads to more decomposition until there is so little oxygen left in the water that it can no longer support life.

3 Plant A, lacking in potassium, needs potassium-rich fertiliser.
Plant B, lack of nitrogen, needs nitrogen-rich fertiliser.
Plant C, lack of phosphate, needs phosphate-rich fertiliser.
Plant D, lack of magnesium, needs magnesium-rich fertiliser.

25 Watering holes

I Support, stomata, transpiration, waxy.

2

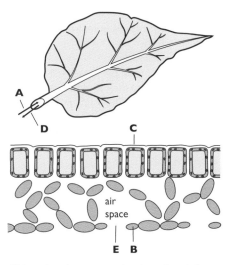

3 a Water loss by evaporation in a plant is known as transpiration.

b Transpiration is more rapid in hot, dry and windy conditions.

c Plants keep relatively cool in hot sun because transpiration cools them down.

d Transpiration also creates a risk that the plant will lose too much water and wilt.

4 a Lower concentration of water molecules inside

membrane bag than outside it. Lower concentration of sugar molecules outside bag than inside it. Water molecules move into bag by diffusion along a concentration gradient through the partially permeable membrane. The sugar molecules are too large to pass through the membrane by diffusion and so the imbalance of molecules, and so the diffusion gradient for the water molecules, is maintained. Water continues to move into the bag and so the water level in the tube rises.

b Useful because root hair cell is similar to the partially permeable membrane bag. Water moves into the cell from the soil along a concentration gradient but sugars etc cannot leave the cell.

c Sugars such as sucrose affect the osmotic balance. So a build-up of these sugars in cells would lead to the movement of water into those cells by osmosis. This water movement might not be useful to the plant. Starch is not osmotically active, so carbohydrates can be stored in plant cells in the form of starch without causing water to move into the cells as well. Plants can move water internally by converting sucrose to starch or vice versa.

d Active transport as it uses energy.

e The constant evaporation of water from the leaves means that water molecules are pulled up through the plant transport system as the water molecules stick together. Thus water is constantly being removed from the roots, raising the concentration of the cytoplasm in the root hair cells and thus causing water to move into those cells by osmosis from the soil water around the roots.

f The large surface area of the roots means that many root cells are in close contact with soil and soil water. This means lots of water can move by osmosis from the soil into the roots.

26 Absorbing roots

I a Through the roots in the soil.

b Xylem

c Phloem

d Xylem

e Phloem cells are living, xylem cells are dead.

2 a Transpiration is the process by which a plant loses water from the leaves by evaporation through the stomata.

b The waxy cuticle

c Very little effect as the waxy cuticle is on the top surface.

d Most stomata on the bottom surface of leaves. Vaseline on lower surface would cover stomata, preventing the loss of water by evaporation and so slowing the rate at which water is taken up.

e The air bubble would move rapidly towards the plant because the fan would increase the rate of water lost by evaporation from the surface of the leaves and so the uptake of water would increase.

f The apparatus is measuring uptake of water, not water lost by transpiration. A small amount of the water taken up will be used for photosynthesis etc.

3 **a** A root cortex, B phloem, C xylem, D root epidermis, E root hair cell, F movement of water, G soil water, H soil particle.

b The concentration of solutes in the soil water is much lower than in the cytoplasm of the root hair cells, so water moves into the root hair cell by osmosis. The root hair cell has a large surface area so that as much water as possible moves in. The water then moves across the root from one cell to another by osmosis across a gradient of water potential until it reaches the xylem in the centre of the root.

c Transpiration

d Mineral ions need to be moved into the root hair cells against a concentration gradient. A process of active transport which uses energy from cellular respiration is needed to move the mineral ions in.

4 **a** Water is lost from the leaves by evaporation through the stomata. Water moves into the roots of a plant by osmosis from the soil water into the root hair cell and across the plant to the xylem. The water is pulled up the xylem in a constant stream from the roots to replace the water lost from the leaves by evaporation (a labelled diagram may be used as an answer).

b Description to include:
• either weight potometer (plant in polythene bag on balance) – limitations: not very accurate as limited by balance
• or volume potometer (water-filled tube, plant shoot, scale, reservoir, air bubble, vaseline to seal joints, diagram helpful), must be set up under water – limitations: measuring water uptake from stem, evaporation from leaves, not true transpiration, difficult to set up – any valid point.

27 Plant growth responses

1 Stimuli, light, gravity, growing, hormones, tropisms.
2 **a** towards, phototropism
b away from, geotropism
c towards, hydrotropism
d towards, geotropism

3 a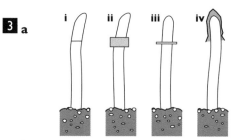

b **i** Tip makes hormone in response to one-sided light, passes down to the growing region. Shoot grows more on the dark side and so bends towards the light.
ii As **i**, the hormone is water-soluble and passes through the agar jelly.
iii Hormone cannot pass through glass so the shoot remains growing upright.
iv Light does not reach the tip of the shoot through the foil cap, so the shoot continues to grow upright.

c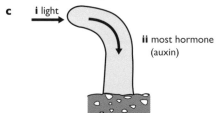
i light
ii most hormone (auxin)

28 Plant reproduction

1 Asexually, sexually, flowers, pollinated, wind, brightly coloured, scent
2 **a** From a runner, a special stem from the parent plant.
b Asexual
c By sexual reproduction.
d The new plants from the packet will be similar, but not identical, to their parents as each one will be genetically different. The plants produced by asexual reproduction will be identical to their parents.
3 **a** Sexual: sex cells produced, fertilisation involved, variation in offspring, good in a changing environment.
Asexual: no sex cells produced, no fertilisation involved, no variation in offspring, good in a stable environment.
b **i** asexual   **ii** bulb
iii Swollen bases of leaves filled with stored food. Buds protected in the centre. Bulbs overwinter underground allowing plant to grow next season. Form new secondary bulbs as form of asexual reproduction.
4 **a** **i** Runners come from stems, new identical plant forms where runner touches the ground.
ii Tubers – swollen food-filled ends of stems form under the ground. Have small buds known as 'eyes' and new plant can be produced from each bud.

b Piece of stem with few leaves cut from healthy plant, put in damp compost/ water until roots grow and then planted on to become a full-sized plant (extra mark for mention of hormone rooting powder). Asexual reproduction because no sex cells, new plant identical to parent plant etc.

5 a a petals, b stigma, c style, d carpel, e ovary, f ovules, g sepals, h filament, i anther, j stamen

b The transfer of pollen grains from the anther to the stigma. It can occur within the same flower (self-pollination) or between different flowers (cross-pollination).

c Insects – it has large brightly coloured petals and the sex organs are inside the petals.

6 a

feathery stigmas to catch more pollen

ovary containing ovules

flower stalk

small petals

anther exposed to wind so pollen can be blown away easily

b

Feature of flower	Type of flower	
	insect pollinated	wind pollinated
position of stamens	enclosed within flower so that insect must make contact	exposed so that wind can easily blow pollen away
position of stigma	enclosed within flower	exposed to catch pollen blowing in wind
type of stigma	sticky so pollen grains attach from insects	feathery to catch pollen grains blowing in wind
size of petals	large to attract insects	small
colour of petals	bright to attract insects	not bright
nectaries	present – nectar is a 'reward' for insects	absent
pollen grains	small, sticky grains to stick to insects' bodies	light, inflated grains to carry in the wind

29 Fertilisation and dispersal

1 a The fusion of a male and a female sex cell or gamete.

b B1, D2, C3, E4, A5

2 a The spreading of seeds from the parent plant.

b To avoid competition for nutrients, water, light etc between the parent plant and the offspring and between the seedlings.

c Plum – fleshy sweet fruit is good to eat, eaten by animals, seeds pass through body or thrown away. Cocklebur – dispersed by animals by attaching to the coat with hooks, carried along until animal grooms and removes burs or they fall off. Maple – wind dispersal, the wings allow the fruit to catch the wind and 'fly' a considerable distance from the parent tree.

3 a Food store for the young plant as it germinates.

b The embryo root. **c** The embryo shoot.

d The wall of the ovule which forms a tough, protective seed coat.

4 a Parachutes, wings, very small and light.

b

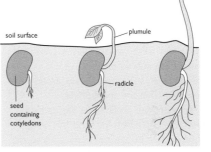

leaves

soil surface

plumule

seed containing cotyledons

radicle

5 a Warmth for efficient enzyme action, water for chemical reactions to take place in solution and for hydrolysis reactions, oxygen for respiration.

b Any appropriate demonstration which shows awareness of the need to control other variables, provide a control etc.

30 Community life

1 Community, all of the living organisms that share a habitat.
Predators, animals that kill and eat other animals.
Prey, animals that are eaten by other animals.
Population, a group of organisms of the same species living in an area.

2 Plants, producers, animals, consumers, primary consumers, secondary consumers.

3 a 140

b 35

c Because of the very harsh winter which killed them with the cold and lack of food.

d 3 years

e Most of the insects would have been killed in the very cold winter of 1963, but they would have begun to recover in 1964.

f The wren population would not be able to recover until the insect population did, because the wrens rely on eating the insects to survive and reproduce. As the insect population increased again, so did the wrens.

4 a It drops significantly.

b Possibly because there are a lot of lynxes eating the snowshoe hares.

c It could be that there are other predators of the hares which are not shown on this graph, or that the food supply of the hares rises and falls affecting the numbers of hares it can support.

31 What is eating what?

1 Energy, photosynthesis, animals, food chains, producer

2 A primrose, rabbit, stoat

B tiny water plants, water fleas, stickleback, pike

C grass, cow, human

D tiny sea plants, fish, seal, polar bear

E rose bush, aphid, ladybird, blue tit

3 a Arctic moss and plants, because they use energy from the Sun to make food and they provide the energy for all the animals in the food web.

b Insects, fish and tundra birds

c Marine birds, seals, polar bears, arctic foxes

d Any three that are appropriate.

e Polar bears and arctic foxes would be in greater competition for food, but numbers of fish would be greater as no seals to eat them. The fish would be eaten more by polar bears in the absence of the seals. The plant numbers might fall due to the increased fish. The numbers of the organisms would fluctuate until a new balance is reached.

f Food webs show how food chains are interconnected, real systems are usually more complex than single chains.

4 **a** **i** **ii**

b Because they are the producers.

c As energy is passed along a food chain between organisms, some of it is lost to the environment, so the further along the chain you go the less energy is left to form living tissue and so the fewer organisms there are.

5 a

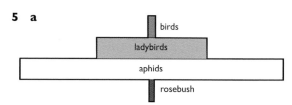

b A pyramid where the blocks represent the mass of the organisms at each level in the food chain.

c **i** Disadvantage: the numbers don't always give a pyramid shape – one rosebush supports many aphids. Advantage: is easy to do, simply have to count.

ii Advantage: measuring biomass usually gives a pyramid as the mass usually decreases along the chain. To measure biomass have to uproot plant, kill everything to find dry mass etc so it is much more complicated and destructive.

32 Biomass and energy

1 a Energy released from biomass during respiration, to be used in movement, warmth, growth of new cells and reproduction.

b Much lost as heat energy, some passed out as waste.

2 a **i** 4.6% **ii** 30% **iii** 13.6%

b Because the mass of the producers has to support the whole pyramid and relatively little energy is transferred from producers to primary consumers as plant material can be difficult to digest.

c Near the top of the chain there is not enough energy to support many carnivores.

d If the animals had been birds or mammals, less energy would have been passed on between the levels. They are warm-blooded and so use a lot of energy to keep warm, which is then lost into the environment so that energy is no longer available to pass on up the chain.

3 This should be marked with regard to the presentation of the arguments, the way they are backed up by science, the appearance of the leaflet, its suitability for the audience of shoppers etc.

4 a A representation of the energy gains and losses by different types of organisms over time.

b It is most accurate because it looks at the actual energy transferred – there is no problem with wet or dry mass etc or destroying the organisms to make measurements. Also because it covers a substantial time period rather than a single snapshot on the day numbers are counted.

c Typical pyramid of energy appropriately labelled.

33 Removing nature's waste

1 Leaves, droppings, decomposed, microorganisms, nutrients, recycled

2

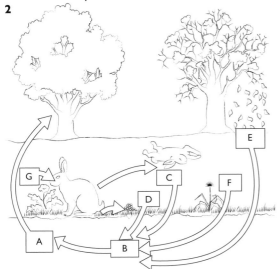

3 Diagram needs to show crop being harvested and removed. Also roots and fertiliser or manure being ploughed into the soil before a new crop is grown.

34 Chemical merry-go-round

1 Respiration, waste product, photosynthesise, decomposed, carbon dioxide.

2

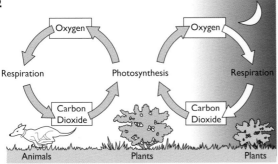

3

A Photosynthesis: plants....   D Decay: carbon dioxide....

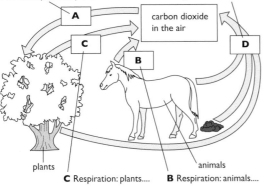

C Respiration: plants....   B Respiration: animals....

4 a The levels go up steadily.

  b A fuel that is made up of the fossilised remains of once-living organisms, e.g. coal, oil.

  c Mainly carbon dioxide (to a lesser extent carbon monoxide, sulphur dioxide etc.)

  d We drive around in cars, burn fossil fuels in power stations etc.

  e Plants take in carbon dioxide in photosynthesis, so cutting down trees reduces the take up of carbon dioxide. Also most of the trees which are cut down are burnt, releasing the carbon dioxide stored in their tissue again.

35 Nutrient cycles

1 a It is needed to make proteins.

  b They always have enough nitrates regardless of how well the soil is fertilised.

2 A nitrifying bacteria, B nitrogen-fixing bacteria in root nodules, C denitrifying bacteria, D nitrogen-fixing bacteria in the soil, E nitrifying bacteria

3 There were two main reasons. Different crops take different nutrients from the soil, so cereals and cabbages will both grow well as they will use different nutrients. The fallow year grows clover which is then ploughed in. Clover forms nitrates in the root nodules, so when it is ploughed in this returns nitrates and other minerals into the soil.

4 a Because it is an important part of the structure of many key biological molecules including proteins, amino acids, DNA, RNA, ATP and many vitamins.

  b **i** As one organism feeds on another, nitrogen containing compounds are passed along the food chain.

    ii The decomposers (microorganisms) break down the tissues of dead organisms and produce ammonia which contains nitrogen. This is then converted to nitrates by other microorganisms.

    iii This takes place in the soil, by free-living bacteria, and in the root nodules of leguminous plants. Bacteria convert nitrogen gas in the air into ammonia which can then be used by the bacteria to make nitrogen compounds such as amino acids. Any excess is used by other organisms.

36 Life in the balance

1 Water, carbon dioxide, dissolved, respiration, photosynthesis.

2 a Producers, green water plants use the energy in sunlight to make food.
Herbivores, animals like the pond snail which feed on pond weed and other water plants.
Carnivores, animals like water boatmen and great diving beetles which eat other animals.
Decomposers, organisms like the waterlouse and various microorganisms which feed on decaying plant and animal remains.

b Producers, herbivores, carnivores, decomposers.

c Producers

3 a Not enough oxygen in the water to keep the fish alive.

b In the light the water plants could photosynthesise and produce oxygen, so the fish survived.

c Now too many fish in the tank, not enough oxygen to support them all.

d The pump made sure there was plenty of oxygen in the tank so it could now support more fish.

4 a Three-quarters of the surface of the Earth is covered with water so it is a very important habitat for living organisms. All living organisms rely on water as a major constituent of their cells.

b

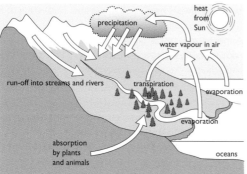

c Heat from the Sun evaporates water from the surface of the oceans, lakes and rivers. Plant transpiration and respiration from all living organisms release water vapour into the air. As air rises it cools and water vapour forms tiny droplets of water to make clouds. As clouds rise over mountains and high ground they cool more and water condenses further to form rain and/or snow. This precipitation falls on the Earth, where it joins the bodies of water or is taken into the bodies of living organisms to start the cycle again.

d Any thoughtful and well argued point which makes sense, even if not correct, e.g. less water in rivers, lakes etc due to more evaporation if the temperatures rises, more water from melting ice caps, warmer air so less precipitation, plants photosynthesising faster in warmer temps so more water taken out of soil.

37 Farming and pest control

I a Provides the right balance of mineral ions needed by plants for maximum growth.

b Provides some of the mineral ions needed by the plants for growth, improves structure of the soil and uses up animal waste

c Enriches the nitrate content of the soil using the nitrogen-fixing bacteria in the root nodules.

d Allows control of mineral ions available to the plants along with temperature, carbon dioxide

levels and light levels to ensure maximum yields and rapid growth.

2 Pests, livestock, yield, third, stored, pesticides, biological.

3 a

Chemical	Use
molluscicide	kills molluscs e.g. snails and slugs
herbicide	kills plants/weeds
fungicide	kills fungi e.g. moulds
insecticide	kills insect pests

b Advantages: kill specific pests, give increase in yields and so increase in income.
Disadvantages: pests may become resistant to a pesticide so need to find another one, pesticides can be expensive and so reduce profits, pesticides can cause environmental damage.

4 a Biological control uses another organism to reduce the numbers of a pest organism.

b Small numbers of pests do not have any noticeable effect on yields. Problems arise when pest numbers get too large. Biological pest control uses another organism – for example a natural predator – to reduce pest numbers to a level which does not have a negative impact on the crop. It does not completely eradicate the pest.

c Appropriate description of the general principle of the methods along with suitable examples.

5 a The DDT levels increase because at each level the organisms eat lots of the smaller organisms, e.g. small fish eat many plankton and the DDT in each plankton adds up to a higher level in the small fish. Then the large fish eats lots of small ones and the DDT is added again etc.

b Would want to see that it is broken down within the food chain, that it does not get passed along in increasing concentrations to cause damage to large consumers. Also that it is not transferred to people. Any other valid point.

38 Food production and forestry

I a Catching more fish than can be replaced by the natural breeding of that species year after year.

b Around 1960.

c Around 2045.

d Answer appropriate to the date from the graph, 40+%.

e Any sensible suggestions, e.g. banning fishing of threatened species completely, restricting net sizes so only larger fish caught, banning fishing during breeding seasons, only allowing fishermen to catch strict quotas.

2 a Three from: salmon, trout, tuna, sea bream and increasingly cod.

b Fish kept in large tanks/enclosures so water quality can be monitored. Diet carefully controlled, fish protected against predators and pesticides used to kill parasites. In some fish farms water temperature and oxygen levels controlled. Selective breeding for fast growth.

c Spread of disease higher than normal, excessive use of antibiotics, pollution from the fish waste, pesticides used to control parasites can affect other fish, farmed fish may escape and cross-breed with wild stock, farmed fish may be fed on fish-meal made from wild fish!

3 a Looking after the environment so that it can be used for many years to come or words to that effect.

b Cattle, sheep or goats feeding on an area for too long so that all the soil vegetation is cropped away or trampled.

c The roots of grass and other plants bind the soil together. If the plants are all killed by overgrazing, the soil may be blown away by the wind or washed away by heavy rain, so it is unprotected against erosion of any sort. This can turn fertile land into a desert.

d Any sensible suggestions, e.g. education to help people understand it is better not to have too many animals on one area of land, or to allow them to graze the same area for too long.

4 a Around 30 ppm.

b Any sensible suggestions, to include burning fossil fuels in cars, burning fossil fuels in power stations, CFCs from fridges, deforestation.

c In winter, trees respire but don't photosynthesise (lost their leaves), so CO_2 levels go up. In spring and summer trees get new leaves and photosynthesise faster than they respire so overall CO_2 levels go down.

d i Plant roots bind the soil together and the tree canopy protects the soil from the worst of the wind and rain. Once the trees have gone, the soil is easily removed by wind and rain.

ii Once the soil is exposed, more water lands on it and minerals are leached away. Also each year in a forest the leaves fall and rot, restoring minerals to the soil, but after deforestation this doesn't happen.

iii Trees take up large amounts of water from the soil and release it into the atmosphere in the transpiration stream as part of the water cycle. When the trees are lost, far less water returns to the atmosphere.

iv Trees remove carbon dioxide from the atmosphere for photosynthesis during the months they have leaves. They also produce oxygen as a waste product of photosynthesis. They don't use all they produce, so they add to atmospheric oxygen and remove carbon dioxide as they make sugars. This carbon dioxide is then tied up in plant material for many years. Once the trees are removed, less carbon dioxide is removed (so more in the atmosphere) and less oxygen produced.

39 A global threat

1 a Any three from: water vapour, carbon dioxide, methane, nitrous oxide, CFCs.

b Without the greenhouse effect the surface of the Earth would be too cold for life.

c Article should cover all the main issues thoroughly and clearly in an interesting way which people would read.

2 a Burning petrol and diesel in vehicle engines.

b It is poisonous. It joins with the haemoglobin in the blood and stops it carrying oxygen to the tissues. If you breathe in too much carbon monoxide it can kill you.

3 a Because hot water is provided from the power station, people don't have to use more fossil fuels or electricity generated from burning fossil fuels in power stations to heat water in their homes. This cuts down greatly on the electricity, gas and oil used and so on the carbon dioxide emissions which would result from burning them.

b Any valid points along the lines of cutting down unnecessary journeys, switching off electric lights etc when not in use.

40 Polluting the air

1 Fossil fuels, pollution, sulphur dioxide, power stations, energy, acid rain.

2

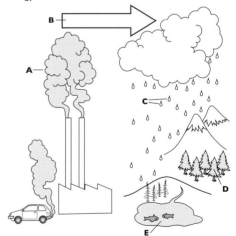

3 a Bar chart correctly drawn.

b Hungary and Finland

c Netherlands and Switzerland

d Because sulphur dioxide pollution is carried in the wind from countries which do produce a lot, and falls as acid rain on Poland and Sweden.

e Reducing sulphur content of fuels, removing sulphur dioxide from emissions in industry.

4 a Bar chart correctly drawn.

b Area A is an inner city, area B a country village.

c Cities contain a lot more cars and factories – sources of air pollution so expect city air to be much more polluted than country air.

41 Water pollution

1 Inorganic fertilisers/organic waste, organic waste/inorganic fertilisers, eutrophication, anoxic, microorganisms, thermal, power stations, oxygen.

2 a Something that can be broken down and used as food by microorganisms.

b Human population growing, more people, more waste to be dumped in the water.

c Because there is plenty of food so the microorganisms can grow and reproduce.

d Means the level of oxygen falls as it is used up. As the number of bacteria increases, they are all taking oxygen from the water so the level of oxygen dissolved in the water begins to fall.

e As the sewage pollution leads to oxygen depletion by the microorganisms, the other organisms die from lack of oxygen in the water.

3 a Nitrates were washed into the stream from the soil which has been fertilised.

b It would increase.

c The nitrates are used up as the plant population increases, then increase again as the plants start to die and nitrates are released again as the decay.

d To increase as the plants die off.

e Microorganisms use up a lot of oxygen as they decompose dead plants.

f As the oxygen levels fall the fish would die, making the situation worse as they are then decomposed in turn by microorganisms.

g Eutrophication

h It could be from the nearby farm, or added to from other farms, or from cattle slurry washing into the stream, or from sewage getting into the stream.

42 Similarities and differences

1 Parents, offspring, genes, chromosomes, characteristics.

2 Nucleus, contains the chromosomes carrying thousands of genes.

Sperm, contains the chromosomes which carry genes from the father.

Egg, contains the chromosomes which carry genes from the mother.

Fertilised egg, contains chromosomes from both parents.

3 a Deoxyribonucleic acid

b A section of DNA code, the sequence of bases that codes for a particular characteristic.

c Guanine with cytosine, adenine with thymine.

4 a Double helix with ribose–phosphate backbone to each strand, and strands joined by pairs of bases.

b Because the bases always pair in the same way – guanine with cytosine, alanine with thymine.

c T-A-C-A-A-A-T-G-G-C-T-A-C-C-C-T-T-G-A-C-T

d The bases are 'read' in threes when they are used to code for amino acids.

e Start, phenylalanine, threonine, aspartic acid, glycine, asparagine, stop.

43 Mutation

1 Mutations, genes, variation, radiation, mutagens.

2 a To protect them from radiation which can cause mutations.

b It would be easy for them to be exposed to high levels of radiation which can cause mutations in any children they might have or cancer.

3 a Smoking increases your risk of dying from lung cancer.

b Smoking increases the levels of these chemicals in your body.

c Cigarette smoke is taken into the lungs so the concentration of carcinogenic chemicals is particularly high in that tissue.

4 a Suitably plotted graph.

b It shows that the rate of mutation increases as the dose of radiation goes up.

5 a Mutations in the reproductive cells can lead to infertility or to the birth of babies suffering from genetic abnormalities.

b Mutations in normal body cells can give rise to cancers.

6 After the first application of a pesticide, the majority of the insects are killed. Most of the insects which survive will stay alive because of a mutation which occurred either in the egg, the sperm or the fertilised egg from which they developed that makes them resistant to the pesticide. These insects live and reproduce, so that when the population is again exposed to the pesticide, most of the insects will be resistant descendants of the original survivors and so will be unaffected by the spray. Some however will have mutated again and lost their resistance, and they will be killed by the pesticide.

44 Division and inheritance

1 a

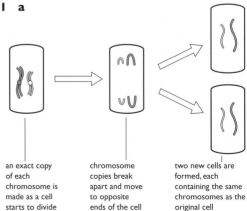

an exact copy of each chromosome is made as a cell starts to divide

chromosome copies break apart and move to opposite ends of the cell

two new cells are formed, each containing the same chromosomes as the original cell

b So that the new cells are exactly the same as the old ones, so the new individual is made up of the same unique cells and so the cells all carry the right information to enable them to do their jobs.

c It is the way the body makes new cells to replace old worn out ones and also heals damaged tissue.

2 a In human reproduction meiosis is important in the formation of the sex cells. It halves the number of chromosomes so, when the sex cells join, a normal cell with 46 chromosomes results. It also introduces variation. After fertilisation mitosis is important in the formation of the millions of cells needed to make up the new individual.

b Mitosis is important for making the new cells needed to give the cuttings roots and then for normal growth to continue. Meiosis plays no part.

3 a 46   **b** 23   **c** Meiosis

d In the ovaries and testes

e

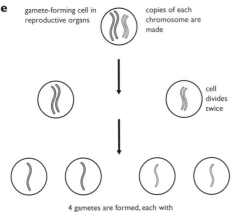

gamete-forming cell in reproductive organs

copies of each chromosome are made

cell divides twice

4 gametes are formed, each with a single set of chromosomes

4 a Bar chart correctly drawn.

b Height, because height varied relatively little whether the twins were brought up together or apart, whereas their mass was similar if they were brought up together and fed the same food but not so similar when they were brought up apart.

c Can give credit for any answer well supported in the explanation. However the expected answer would be: Yes, because non-identical twins and siblings who are not twins are not particularly similar in height and there is a big difference between them and identical twins, however they are brought up. With body mass, identical twins brought up apart show the same difference in mass as the other two groups, showing a much bigger influence of environment on body mass.

d Because identical twins themselves are relatively rare, so identical twins who are separated and brought up apart for long periods of time and then find out about each other so comparisons can be made are very rare indeed.

45 Patterns of inheritance

1 gene, unit of genetic information linked to a particular characteristic

allele, gene which has different forms

dominant allele, allele which controls the development of a characteristic even when it is present on only one of a pair of chromosomes

recessive allele, allele that controls the development of a characteristic only if it is present on both of a pair of chromosomes

homozygous, when both chromosomes in a pair contain the same allele of a gene

heterozygous, when both chromosomes in a pair contain different alleles of a gene

2 a Sandy **rr** – she cannot roll her tongue so must be homozygous recessive.

b **Rr** – Tom must have a recessive gene to pass on even though he shows the dominant character trait.

c **Rr** or **RR** – Tom has passed on a dominant gene.

3 a Parents   **Tt**   ×   **tt**
Gametes   **T**   **t**   ×   **t**   **t**
Offspring   **Tt**   **Tt**   **tt**   **tt**
      Manx   normal

b Parents   **Tt**   ×   **Tt**
Gametes   **T**   **t**   ×   **T**   **t**
Offspring **TT**   **Tt**   **Tt**   **tt**
Expected ratio: 3:1

c Ratio of Manx kittens actually born is 2 Manx : 1 normal, because the homozygous Manx kittens die before birth.

4 a Parents   XY   ×   XY
Gametes   X   Y   ×   X   Y
Offspring XX   XY   XX   XY
Expected ratio: 1:1

b i 20

ii Because a Barr body comes when one of two X chromosomes is deactivated. Only women have two X chromosomes, so only women have Barr bodies.

46 Genetic problems

1 a Parents   **WW**   ×   **ww**
Gametes   **W**   **W**   ×   **w**   **w**
Offspring   **Ww**
     all smooth and round

b Parents   **Ww**   ×   **ww**
Gametes   **W**   **w**   ×   **w**   **w**
Offspring **Ww**   **Ww**   **ww**   **ww**
   smooth and round   wrinkled

2 a **C** normal allele, **c** cystic fibrosis allele (or something appropriate)
Parents   **Cc** (Frankie)   **CC** (Annie)
Gametes   **C**   **c**   ×   **C**   **C**
Possible offspring   **CC**   **Cc**   **CC**   **Cc**

There is no chance of them having a child with cystic fibrosis, although some of their children may be carriers of the faulty allele.

b Neither have faulty gene: **CC** × **CC**
all offspring **CC**
One has faulty gene: same as in part **a**
offspring **CC** or **Cc**
Both are carriers: **Cc** × **Cc**
Possible offspring: **Cc, Cc , cC, cc**
A 1:4 chance of producing a child with cystic fibrosis.

3 a **D** for dwarfism and **d** for normal (or something appropriate)
A **Dd**   B **dd**   C **Dd**

b Could be that the embryo was homozygous dominant, which is lethal.

Parents	**Dd**		×	**Dd**	
Gametes	**D**	**d**	×	**D**	**d**
Offspring	**DD**	**Dd**		**Dd**	**dd**
	(dies, could be cause of miscarriage)	achondroplastic dwarfs		normal height	

47 Natural selection in action

1 a Different genetic variations exist in the same population.
b Yes, more obvious to predators.
c Yes, birds with white feathers are more likely to survive the winter without being eaten and so are more likely to survive and breed.
d Yes, brown birds are mutations and are relatively unsuccessful so they stay as a minority in the population.

2 a 2 years, to 1917
b 1930 or 1933 would be acceptable.
c 1937, 22 years from the first appearance of the disease.
d When the disease first appeared virtually all of the oysters were wiped out. Of those that remained, some were lucky, and may have succumbed to the disease later, others must have possessed a mutation which gave them immunity to the disease. This mutation allowed a tiny number of oysters to survive and become a breeding colony. Once established, these oysters bred rapidly to restore the oyster numbers with oysters which were now immune to the disease.

3 The theory of natural selection says that individual organisms within a species may show a wide range of variation because of differences in their genes. Individuals with characteristics most suited to their environment are more likely to survive and breed successfully, and the genes which have enabled these individuals to survive are then passed on to the next generation. This explains the situation with the Galapagos finches. Birds arrived on a particular island or an area of an island from the mainland blown by a storm or similar. Those birds with beaks best suited to a particular food type (either one which was very common in the area or something not exploited by other animals) would be most successful and most likely to breed, passing on the genes for the slightly modified beak. Over many generations this effect would be magnified, until the birds formed separate breeding colonies with separate feeding strategies and different beak structures. Each type of finch was particularly successful in its own niche. Breeding isolation would be achieved by distance and also by changing displays which were no longer universally recognised.

4 a Sickle cell disease is inherited. It involves the production of abnormal haemoglobin which cannot carry oxygen properly and which is carried in sickle-shaped red blood cells.

b **H** for normal haemoglobin, **h** for sickle cell disease (or something appropriate)

Parents	**Hh**		×	**Hh**	
Gametes	**H**	**h**	×	**H**	**h**
Offspring	**HH**	**Hh**	**Hh**		**hh**
	normal	mild anaemia			sickle cell anaemia

c i The two children with mild anaemia are most likely to survive in Africa as they will have increased resistance to malaria.

ii The normal child is most likely to survive in the UK as there is no risk from malaria but the anaemia might be a problem.

48 Selecting the best

1 Cuttings, identical, parents, characteristics
2 a Selective breeding.
 b i lay more eggs
 ii tamer, much more meat, grow faster
 iii cows from wild cattle
 iv tamer, smaller, more obedient
 v grow more, bigger potatoes
 vi any garden fruit e.g. apples, strawberries
 vii larger more colourful flowers, stronger scent
3 a It is increasing at a very rapid rate.
 b We need to be able to feed all the people.
 c Bar chart correctly drawn.
 d Potatoes and citrus fruits
 e Otherwise many of the extra crops grown will be lost to disease. By making crops disease resistance the yield can be increased.

4 a There is a lot of cheap milk available for milk and milk products.
 b The big increase in milk production is in areas like Europe, when the main need for extra food is in the developing world. So in Europe there is a milk lake – more milk produced than used. Also some animals that produce high yields of milk suffer health problems such as mastitis.
 c Cross two particularly large parents with a good meat yield, and then cross the offspring again with

particularly large animals etc. Don't breed from animals with lighter carcasses.

49 High technology breeding

1 a Traditional cuttings uses parts of whole stems and roots, but tissue culture uses minute collections of cells as the starting point.

   b Answers should include: large numbers of genetically identical plants (clones) from just one plant'; can produce large numbers of new plants that might be difficult to produce from seeds or traditional cuttings; produce new plants all through the year by growing them in the laboratory; store large numbers of plants easily.

   c There is no variety in the population so if one plant cannot cope with a change in conditions, none of them will be able to and they will all die.

2 Udder cells removed from sheep 1 and cultured. → Mature ovum taken from sheep 2 and nucleus removed. → Nucleus taken from cultured udder cell and placed in empty ovum. → Mild electric shock applied. → Nucleus from sheep 1 fuses with empty egg from sheep 2 and begins to divide to form an embryo. → Cloned embryo is transferred into uterus of sheep 3. → Lamb born to sheep 3 is clone of sheep 1.

3 a Selective breeding involves crossing several generations of animals or plants to improve a particular feature. In genetic manipulation, a gene for a desired characteristic is altered or added directly.

   b Can guarantee all the cloned offspring of a genetically modified organism will carry the new desired gene. Natural reproduction might lose it!

   c Reducing variety in the gene pool, making it more difficult for a particular animal or plant to cope with changing conditions. Or any other valid and well-argued point.

4 a Both allow large numbers of genetically identical individuals to be produced from good parent stock much faster and more reliably than would be possible using traditional techniques.

   b Cloning plants uses bits of the adult plant as the raw material for the cloning. Animal cloning as it is used at the moment involves embryos as the raw material, although this may change in the future. Dolly was produced from a mammary gland cell.

   c There are more and more people in the world needing feeding so techniques for reproducing high-yielding plants and animals are always needed. Also in developed countries people demand high quality but cheap food, so techniques that reproduce valuable animals and plants more quickly are valued.

50 Using microorganisms

1 a Any appropriate things.

   b i Yeast: individual cells, cell walls, nucleus, obtain food from other organisms, reproduce asexually; mould: long hyphal threads, nuclei, cell walls, obtain food from other organisms, reproduce asexually.

      ii The way they feed and reproduce.

   c Clear comparisons showing differences and similarities in structure, feeding, reproduction etc.

2 Aerobic: sugar + oxygen → carbon dioxide + water
anaerobic: sugar → carbon dioxide + ethanol

3 Barley grains soaked and kept warm → germination of barley, enzymes break down starch stores to sugary solution → sugary solution extracted from barley → yeast added along with hops → fermentation takes place → beer left to clear when yeast has used up all the sugar → beer develops flavour → beer bottled, canned or barrelled.

4 a So enzymes in yeast work at the best rate.

   b i Continues fermenting ii Carbon dioxide

5 Warm milk → starter culture added → kept warm → bacteria grow, reproduce and make lactic acid → lactic acid makes milk clot and solidify, while bacteria keep texture smooth.

6 a Can be grown in big fermenters, relatively cheap, no animal rights issues, can be genetically engineered, produce huge amounts of stuff etc.

   b Air supply to provide oxygen for aerobic respiration; stirring paddles to keep microorganisms and culture medium mixed so food and oxygen evenly distributed and give even temp; water-cooled jacket to remove excess heat; measuring instruments to monitor pH to keep conditions at optimum for microorganisms, inlet pipes to supply nutrients etc, steam inlet for sterilising between batches so no contamination. Any other valid point.

7 a Metabolism of millions of microorganisms produces heat.

   b Concentration drops as microorganisms grow and divide use up oxygen in respiration.

   c Build-up of carbon dioxide from respiration lowers the pH.

8 *Penicillium* mould mixed with medium containing sugars from corn steep and oxygen supplied → kept warm (24 °C) and stirred with paddles → 40 h mould grows extensively, nutrients used up → next 140 h, penicillin made → broth filtered to remove yeast → the penicillin extracted by dissolving in organic solvents, then water and then crystallised.

51 Genetic modification

1 a Bacteria can be cultured in very large numbers, don't need expensive conditions, make large quantities of pure chemicals such as insulin or human growth hormone, any other valid point.

   b Engineered organisms might 'escape' and cause disease, engineered organisms might cross breed with wild organisms, unnatural, any other valid point

2 Genetically modified plants can be produced to give better yields so that more food is produced, or disease resistant varieties so that less food is lost to disease, or containing pesticide so that less money has to be invested in spraying so farmers can afford to grow more. Any other valid points.

3 **a**

Stage 1 The gene that makes growth hormone is cut from the DNA

Gene for making growth hormone

special enzymes act like molecular scissors.....

....."cutting out" gene from rest of DNA

human DNA

Stage 2 The human gene is inserted into bacterial DNA

enzymes "cut" bacterial DNA .....

..... and then insert human gene

human gene for making growth hormone

    b It is pure, free from any contamination. Can be produced in large amounts relatively easily and cheaply.

4 **a** Insulin allows glucose into the cells and controls the blood sugar concentration.

    b More effective because human, cleaner so no risk of contamination, supply can be matched to demand in production lines.

5 Required gene cut from DNA of other organism using restriction enzymes.
Plasmid isolated from bacteria *Agrobacterium tumefaciens*.
Plasmid cut open using restriction enzymes.
Cut plasmid and desired gene joined by ligase enzyme.
Leaf discs cut from plant to be modified and floated on liquid containing the modified plasmids.
Some of the discs take up the modified plasmid.
The discs are cultivated on a nutrient medium to form plantlets.
Plantlets grown into whole plants containing foreign gene.

52 Biotechnology

1 **a** Answers will vary but should include points such as: produce human proteins needed to treat diseases more easily than ever before, improve food production.

    b **i** Height is perceived to be a good thing. People look up to taller people, so parents might want to buy that advantage for their children.

      ii Athletes want to perform better all the time. If growth hormone increases their muscles they will be able to perform better, possibly without this 'cheating' being detected.

     iii Mark with respect to the reasons and their link to the opinions expressed.

    c Mark according to presentation of arguments and logic, whichever opinion is expressed.

2 **a** Bacteria are hardly regarded as living and not seen as having rights. Some people feel that mammals are being exploited when they are engineered in this way.

    b Mark according to presentation of arguments and logic, whichever opinion is expressed.

Chemistry answers

1 Safety in the lab

1. **a** conical flask **b** mixing liquids
    c test tube **d** small-scale reactions
    e filter funnel **f** filtering/transferring liquids
    g beaker **h** large-scale reactions
    i pipette **j** accurate measurement of liquid volume
    k thermometer **l** measurement of temperature
2. **a** irritates the skin, makes it go red and blister
    b copper(II) oxide
    c attack and destroy living tissues
    d hydrochloric acid **e** poisonous, can cause death
    f mercury **g** catches fire easily **h** petrol
    i provide oxygen to let other chemicals burn more fiercely **j** hydrogen peroxide
    k similar to toxic but unlikely to kill you
    l lead(II) nitrate
3. Table will be completed with a variety of substances.

2 Inside the atom

1. Subatomic, nucleus, protons, electrons.
2. **a** Protons, large, positive. Electrons, small, negative.
    b No charge (neutral).
    c Protons and neutrons.
    d

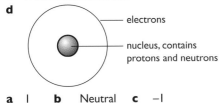

    electrons

    nucleus, contains protons and neutrons

3. **a** 1 **b** Neutral **c** −1
4. Protons, protons, atomic, neutrons, mass, electrons.
5. **a** He: atomic number 2, mass number 4
    b F: atomic number 9, mass number 19
    c Fe: atomic number 26, mass number 56
    d U: atomic number 92, mass number 238
6. **a** 3 **b** 3 **c** 11 **d** 12
    e 48 **f** 36 **g** 82 **h** 125
7. **a** Same number of protons.
    b Different numbers of neutrons (18 and 20).
    c Carbon (C) as it has 6 protons.

8 **a**

Element	Atomic number	Mass number	Number of neutrons
H	1	1	0
He	2	4	2
Li	3	7	4
Be	4	9	5
B	5	11	6
C	6	12	6
N	7	14	7
O	8	16	8
F	9	19	10
Ne	10	20	10

   b Graph correctly plotted and suitable line of best fit.
   c They are roughly equal.

d No. There are larger numbers of neutrons in large atoms.

3 Atomic structure

1. Electrons, shell, energy, eight.
2. A $^{7}_{3}$Li (lithium) 2, 1 B $^{12}_{6}$C (carbon) 2, 4
    C $^{20}_{10}$Ne (neon) 2, 8 D $^{23}_{11}$Na (sodium) 2, 8, 1
3. Electrons shown on diagrams: B 2, 3 O 2, 6
    Mg 2, 8, 2 Ar 2, 8, 8 K 2, 8, 8, 1

4 **a** A helium B argon C neon
   b Full outer shells.
   c They are unreactive.
   d and **e**

   f Both are the same – like neon.
   g A full outer shell gives great stability.
   h Sodium ion is positive, fluorine ion is negative.

5 Sami is right – the reactants and the products have the same combined mass. The law of conservation of mass states that the total mass at the end of a reaction is the same as total mass at the beginning of the reaction. The atoms have simply been arranged into new substances. Add up the numbers of the different types of atom on both sides of the equation and you will have the same numbers – so they will have the same mass, however they are arranged.

4 Solids, liquids and gases

1. Particles, solids, squashed, gases, closer
2. **a** fixed **b** not fixed **c** not fixed
3. **a** A gas B liquid C solid
    b solid **c** gas **d** solid
    e liquid and gas **f** gas
4. **a** ...the forces are winning...
    b ...it is evenly balanced...
    c ...motion has won!...
5. **a** Brownian motion
    b The particles of matter are too small to see so you can't see them moving. However, you can see the effect of their movement – the particles bumping into the pollen grains causes movement (Brownian motion) in the pollen grains.

5 Keep them moving

1. **a** In solid ice...
       As ice is heated...
       At 0 °C, the particles...
       The ice melts.
    b 0 °C
    c Stronger – need more energy put in to break them.
2. **a** The water particles in steam...
       If the particles collide...

As the steam cools...
At or below 100 °C...
Clumps of particles stick together...
The steam condenses.

b Weaker. Lower temperature needed to break up clumps of particles.

c The particles move faster and faster – at 100 °C all the bonds start to break and the particles fly apart. The water boils.

3 a Diffused through the air.

b They mix in with the fast-moving air particles, get bounced around and spread out.

c He was the nearest.

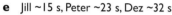

e Jill ~15 s, Peter ~23 s, Dez ~32 s

f 0.2 m s⁻¹

4 a Water particles surround...
Some of the outer salt particles...
The salt and water particles diffuse away...

b Slower – the particles in liquids are moving much more slowly than the particles in gases.

6 Covalent bonding

1 a A bond where a pair of electrons is shared between two atoms.

b i 2   ii 2   iii 1   iv 4

2 a

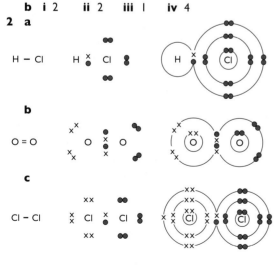

d

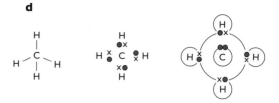

3 a Covalent bonds within covalent substances are very strong but there are only relatively weak forces between the molecules, which means it is relatively easy to separate them and so the boiling and melting points are low.

b There are no free electrons or ions to move and conduct electricity.

4 a

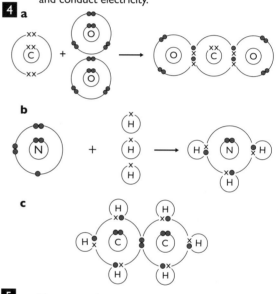

5 a The outer electron shells join together and one pair of electrons (one from each atom) moves around both atoms. Each atom gets a share of a full shell of electrons.

b Covalent.

c

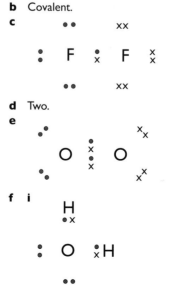

d Two.

e

f i

40

ii

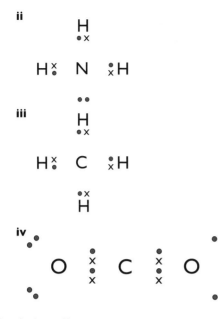

iii

iv

7 Ionic bonding

1 Carbon, molecules, metals, ions.
2 Metallic, positive.   Non-metallic, negative.
3 a i KCl ii K_2O iii $CaCl_2$ iv CaO
  b 1   c 2   d 1
  e i $FeCl_2$ ii $FeCl_3$ iii Cu_2O iv CuO
4 a Ionic substances have much higher melting and boiling points than covalent substances.
  b Ionic substances have high melting and boiling points because strong electrostatic forces between the ions hold them together, so it takes a lot of energy to separate them.
5 a The lone outer electron.
  b Lose its outer electron.
  c 7 in the outer shell – one electron short of a full shell.
  d The sodium atom donates…
    The chlorine atom accepts…
    It becomes a negative ion…
    The oppositely charged ions…
    An ionic bond is formed…
6 a Two outer electrons – easy to lose.
  b Lose the outer electrons.
  c 2+
  d 2
  e $CaCl_2$

f

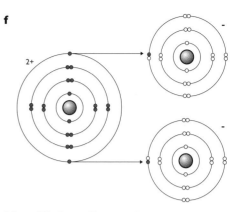

8 Metallic bonding and intermolecular forces

1 Covalent, weak, molecules, low, giant, strong, high.
2 a Solids like iron and lead keep their shape because the particles are held in place by forces.
  b Iron is harder and stronger than lead because the forces between the particles in iron are stronger than lead.
  c Lead is heavier for its size than iron because lead particles weigh more than iron particles.
3 a Ice, solid carbon dioxide, solid methane, solid ammonia and iodine
  b Intermolecular forces hold the molecules together.
4 a Describe intermolecular forces in water in terms of the polar molecule, small positive/negative changes in the molecules and so strong intermolecular forces. In solid state of water, intermolecular forces strong and hold molecules in a crystalline structure – not very dense. As ice melts, some of the intermolecular forces are disrupted so crystalline structure collapses and in liquid water the molecules are closer together, so it is more dense than the solid – hence ice floats.
  b At boiling point molecules moving so fast and with so much energy that the intermolecular forces are broken and the substance becomes a gas. As the gas cools, particles move more slowly, come closer together again and so intermolecular forces begin to come back into play as the water turns back into a liquid.

9 Structures

1 a Gases, liquids or solids with low melting and boiling points; insoluble in water unless they react with it; soluble in organic solvents; don't conduct electricity.
  b Atoms joined by strong covalent bonds, but forces between molecules very weak – so easy to separate and so low melting and boiling points. Can't break attractions between water molecules to enable them to dissolve, but intermolecular forces similar to those in most organic solvents so they can dissolve more easily. No free electrons, so don't conduct electricity

2 **a** Different forms of the same element.
   b Carbon   **c** Red and white
3 **a**

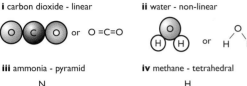

i carbon dioxide - linear

O=C=O or O =C=O

ii water - non-linear

or

iii ammonia - pyramid

N
H   H
H

iv methane - tetrahedral

H
C
H   H
H

   b Related to the way electrons are arranged –
   negative charges repel which pushes the parts of
   the molecule apart.
4 **a** Simple molecular crystals
   b It is a non-metal but it forms solid molecular
   crystals at room temperature.
   c Ice melts to form liquid water. Iodine sublimes
   when it is heated – turns straight to a purple gas.
   It vaporises easily because it has a simple molecular
   structure.
5 **a** Diamond: hard, very high melting and boiling point,
   giant molecular structure so strong carbon–carbon
   covalent bonds between atoms which are very hard
   to break. Insoluble in any solvents. Doesn't conduct
   electricity.
   Graphite: carbon atoms arranged in sheets which
   slide over each other, so soft, lower melting and
   boiling points, insoluble in any solvents. Conducts
   electricity as only forms bonds with three other
   carbon atoms in the graphite sheets which means
   free electrons are available.
   b Diamond is very hard and melts at very high
   temperatures so used for cutting (and as jewellery).
   Graphite relatively soft and slides easily – used as a
   lubricant and in pencils for writing.

10 Structures and bonding

1 Strong intermolecular forces hold the particles
together so a lot of energy is needed to overcome
these forces and allow the substances to melt or boil.
2 **a** A is graphite, B is diamond.
   b Both made from covalently bonded carbon
   atoms only, but the arrangement is different.
   c The same strong covalent bonds have to be
   broken.
   d Diamond has a strong 3D structure. Although
   the bonds are strong within the graphite
   sheets, there are only weak bonds between
   the sheets, which easily slide over one another.
3 **a** Strong electrostatic forces.
   b Hard; high melting point and boiling point.
   c The charged particles are held in place – they
   are not free to move.

d Melting or solution in water.
e No – it just represents the simplest ratio of
   the ions.
4 **a** Metal ions tightly bound in a 'sea' or 'cloud' of
   electrons.
   b The electrons in the cloud are free to move.
   c If the ion lattice is distorted, the electron
   shape reforms in the new position – like
   plasticine with ball-bearings in it.

5

Structure	Ionic	Molecular	Metallic	Giant molecular
melting and boiling points	high	low	high	high
conduction when solid	non-conductor of electricity	non-conductor of electricity	conductor of electricity	conductor of electricity
conduction when liquid	conductor of electricity of electricity	non-conductor	conductor of electricity of	non-conductor electricity
example	any appropriate answer	any appropriate answer	any appropriate answer	any appropriate answer

6 **a**

Substance	Melting point (°C)	Boiling point (°C)	Electrical conductivity at room temperature	Electrical conductivity when liquid	Structure
quartz (silicon dioxide)	1610	2230	very poor	very poor	giant covalent
rubidium fluoride	795	1410	very poor	good	giant ionic
manganese	1244	1962	very good	very good	giant metal

b Quartz: covalent giant lattice, covalent bonds hold the
   molecules together so there are no free electrons
   even when molten so it does not conduct electricity.
   Rubidium fluoride: giant ionic lattice, does not
   conduct electricity when it is solid because there
   are strong attractive forces between the ions
   holding them in place. Once the substance has
   melted or dissolved, the ions are free to move and
   so the substance conducts electricity.
   Manganese: giant metal lattice has a sea of electrons
   which can conduct electricity whether the metal is
   solid or molten.

11 Separating mixtures

1 Atoms, different, element, compound.
2 **a** Filtration
   b Add sand and salt mixture to water and mix
   thoroughly. The salt will dissolve in the water and
   the sand will not. Pour the mixture into the filter

paper in the filter funnel and rinse through with more clear water. Leave to stand. The sand should be left in the filter funnel. The salt is dissolved in the filtrate. (Include suitable diagrams.)

   c Put salt water in an evaporating dish and allow the water to evaporate – may heat gently to speed the process up. This process is evaporation. (Include a suitable diagram.)

3 **a** Crystallisation

   b Different substances usually have different solubilities in the solvent. Dissolve mixture in warm solvent. As temperature falls, the solutes become less soluble in the solvent. The solute which is present in the highest amounts will crystallise out first and can be collected as a pure sample, leaving the impurity still in solution (this assumes that the impurity is the minority substance!).

4 **a** Simple distillation

   b To tell you the temperature at which the gas is being collected.

   c The gas is cooled and condenses so it can be collected. The cold water maintains the cool temperature and removes the heat which is transferred to it.

5 **a** Either: circle of chromatography paper with intense spot of the blue colour in the centre. Position paper over evaporating basin or beaker to support it. Slowly add drops of water to the spot, one at a time. The colours should separate into bands to make a chromatogram.

Or: strip of chromatography paper with spot near one end. Lower into beaker with small amount of water – spot must not go under water. Let water soak up the paper until it almost reaches the top. Coloured spots should have separated out.

   b Different compounds have different-sized molecules. The smallest particles move fastest and so travel further than the larger particles.

12 Formulae and equations

1

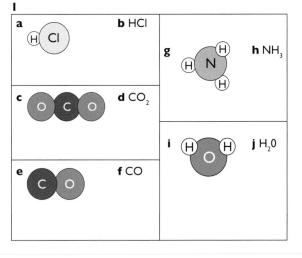

2 **a** 1 × carbon, 4 × hydrogen

   b 8 × carbon, 18 × hydrogen

   c 6 × carbon, 12 × hydrogen, 6 × oxygen

   d 2 × hydrogen, 1 × sulphur, 4 × oxygen

   e 1 × hydrogen, 1 × nitrogen, 3 × oxygen

3 **a** calcium carbonate, $CaCO_3$

   b sodium chloride, $NaCl$

   c aluminium oxide, Al_2O_3

   d lead bromide, $PbBr_2$

4 **a**

Reactants	Products
A hydrogen, oxygen	water
B magnesium, sulphuric acid	magnesium sulphate, hydrogen
C iron, oxygen	iron oxide (rust)
D copper carbonate	copper oxide, carbon dioxide

   b A hydrogen + oxygen → water

      B magnesium → sulphuric acid → magnesium sulphate + hydrogen

      C iron + oxygen → iron oxide

      D copper carbonate → copper oxide + carbon dioxide

5 **a** (s) solid, (l) liquid, (g) gas.

   b **i** Magnesium reacts with oxygen to form magnesium oxide.

     ii Sodium oxide reacts with hydrogen chloride (hydrochloric acid) to give sodium chloride and water.

     iii Copper oxide reacts with sulphuric acid to give copper sulphate and water.

     iv Aluminium reacts with iron oxide (iron(III) oxide) to give aluminium oxide and iron.

     v Magnesium reacts with hydrochloric acid to give magnesium chloride and hydrogen gas.

     vi Sodium reacts with water to give sodium hydroxide solution and hydrogen gas.

13 Chemistry by numbers

1 **a** $HCl + NaOH \rightarrow NaCl + H_2O$

   b Mass, mass.

   c

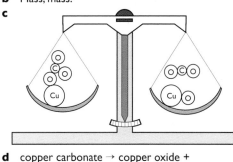

   d copper carbonate → copper oxide + carbon dioxide

e   The mass only appears to have gone down because one of the products (carbon dioxide) is a gas and so has escaped.

f   4.4 g

2 a 4.0 g

   b 0.8 g

   c 4.6 g

3 a i   sodium + bromine → sodium bromide

      ii $2Na + Cl_2 → 2NaCl$

   b i   magnesium + oxygen → magnesium oxide

      ii $2Ca + O_2 → 2CaO$

   c i   sodium + oxygen → sodium oxide

      ii $4K + O_2 → 2K_2O$

4 a i   calcium oxide + hydrochloric acid → calcium chloride + water

      ii $CaO + 2HCl → CaCl_2 + H_2O$

   b i   potassium + water → potassium hydroxide + hydrogen

      ii $2K + 2H_2O → 2KOH + H_2$

   c i   calcium carbonate + hydrochloric acid → calcium chloride + water + carbon dioxide

      ii $CaCO_3 + 2HCl → CaCl_2 + H_2O + CO_2$

   d i   magnesium + hydrochloric acid → magnesium chloride + hydrogen

      ii $Mg + 2HCl → MgCl_2 + H_2$

5 a $Na → Na^+ + e^-$

   b $Cu → Cu^{2+} + 2e^-$

   c $Cl + e^- → Cl^-$

   d $Cl_2 + 2e^- → 2Cl^-$

14 Calculating chemicals

I Elements, relative atomic mass, compound, react.

2 a The weighted average mass of the isotopes of the element. It is measured on a scale on which a carbon-12 atom has a mass of exactly 12 units.

   b It is the average atomic mass of the different isotopes of an element, adjusted for the proportions of the different isotopes found in the element.

3 a 17   **b** 94

   c 160   **d** 46

4 a Reading across the lines

28	56	42	34
32	34	32	28
62	42	56	62

   b CO, N_2 Fe, CaO CaH_2, NaF
   PH_3, H_2O_2 N_2H_4, CH_3OH
   H_2CO_3, MgF_2

15 More chemical calculations

I a ammonium nitrate 28/80 × 100 = 35%;
   ammonium phosphate 28/180 × 100 = 15.6%

   b Ammonium nitrate would be the most effective fertiliser because in a given quantity it contains a higher percentage of nitrogen than ammonium phosphate.

2 a A_r silicon = 28 A_r oxygen = 16
   M_r silicon dioxide   = 28 + (16 × 2)
                = 28 + 32 = 60
   In 60 g of silicon dioxide there are 28 g of silicon, so in 240 g of silicon dioxide there are 28 × 4 g = 112 g silicon.

   b In 60 tonnes silicon dioxide there would be 28 tonnes silicon, so in 360 tonnes silicon dioxide there are 28 × 6 tonnes = 168 tonnes silicon.

3 a The relative atomic or formula mass in grams.

   b Number of moles   = $\dfrac{mass\ (g)}{mass\ of\ 1\ mole\ (g)}$

   c Mass of 1 mole of NaCl is 58.5 g (23 + 35.5), mass of 3 moles is 58.5 × 3 = 175.5 g

   d The mass of 1 mole of $CuSO_4$ is 160 g (64 + 32 + (16 × 4))
   The number of moles   = $\dfrac{320}{160}$ = 2 moles.

4 a $6.02 × 10^{23}$

   b $6.02 × 10^{24}$ (or $60.2 × 10^{23}$)

   c $12.04 × 10^{22}$ (or $1.2 × 10^{23}$)

   d $15.05 × 10^{23}$ (or $1.51 × 10^{24}$)

   e $3.01 × 10^{21}$ (or $0.0301 × 10^{23}$)

5 a The simplest formula which tells you the ratio of the various atoms.

   b The actual numbers of atoms which react to form a molecule.

   c 4.0 – 2.4 = 1.6 so 1.6 g of oxygen are used in the reaction. 2.4 g of Mg reacted with 1.6 g of oxygen.
   The A_r of magnesium is 24, so the number of moles of magnesium reacting is $\dfrac{2.4}{24}$ = 0.1.
   The A_r of oxygen is 16, so the number of moles of oxygen atoms reacting is $\dfrac{1.6}{16}$ = 0.1.
   0.1 moles of magnesium react with 0.1 moles of oxygen. This tells us that 1 atom of magnesium reacts with 1 atom of oxygen – so the empirical formula of the product is MgO.

16 Calculations using moles

I VS_4

2 Fe_3O_4

3 a 1   **b** 0.5   **c** 0.1   **d** 0.25   **e** 0.05

4 a $2Al + Fe_2O_3 → Al_2O_3 + 2Fe$

   b 224 g (4 moles)

5 a $P_4O_{10} + 6H_2O → 4H_3PO_4$

   b i   0.2 moles   ii 19.6 g

6 a $2H_2O + 2NaCl + 2NH_3 + 2CO_2 →$
                $2NH_4Cl + 2NaHCO_3$

   b 50   **c** 4   **d** 17.55 g

7 a The volume occupied by 1 mole of any gas at a given temperature and pressure.

b Rtp is 24 dm^3 or 24 000 cm^3, stp is 22.4 dm^3 or 22 400 cm^3

c 0 °C (273 K) and 1 atmosphere (760 mm Hg)

d The volume of 1 mole of any gas is 24 dm^3 (rtp). So the volume of 0.5 moles of SO_2 is $\frac{24}{2} = 12$ dm^3 (rtp).

One mole of SO_2 has a mass of $32 + (16 \times 2)$ = 64 g. So 0.5 moles has a mass of $\frac{64}{2} = 32$ g.

e Density = $\frac{mass}{volume}$

so the density of sulphur dioxide = $\frac{32}{12}$ = 2.67 g/dm^3

8 First look at the molar relationships between the reacting substances.

$$Zn(s) + 2HCl(aq) \rightarrow ZnCl(aq) + H_2(g)$$

| 65 g | 2 × (1+35.5)g | → | 65 + (2×35.5) g | 2 × 1 g |
| 65 g | 73 g | | 136 g | 2 g |

So 65 g of zinc produce 2 g of hydrogen. 2 g of hydrogen is 1 mole of hydrogen so has a volume of 22.4 dm^3 at stp.

So 65 g zinc gives 22.4 dm^3 hydrogen at stp. Therefore 4 g of zinc give

$\frac{22.4}{65} \times 4 = 1.38$ dm^3 H_2 at stp.

17 Metals, air and water

1 a Copper metal tarnishes slowly in air.

b Gold metal does not tarnish in air.

c Sodium metal reacts very quickly with air.

d When a metal reacts with air it combines with the oxygen in the air to form an oxide.

e When a metal reacts with water it 'steals' the oxygen from water, leaving hydrogen.

2 Lead and copper do not react with water, but iron and magnesium do.

3 Copper tarnishes slowly in air, the resistance of a copper contact may increase with time. This is critical in computers and other electronic equipment, so gold is used here. This is also a good electrical conductor, and it does not tarnish in air. Although expensive, only very small amounts are needed, so the cost of the equipment is not significantly greater.

4 potassium + oxygen → potassium oxide
potassium + water → potassium hydroxide
calcium + oxygen → calcium oxide
calcium + water → calcium hydroxide
zinc + oxygen → zinc oxide
zinc + water → zinc oxide

5 a The reactivity series lists elements – mainly metals – in order of decreasing reactivity. Carbon and hydrogen are non-metals which are included in the series for comparison.

b Different elements react with air (or the oxygen in the air) to produce oxides. They can be ranked by the ease with which they react.
Different elements react with water – cold, hot or steam – to produce metal hydroxides or oxides and hydrogen. Observe ease of reaction.
Different elements react with dilute acids to produce metal salts and hydrogen – again ease of reaction can be observed.

18 Displacement reactions

1 Displacement, zinc, copper, zinc, copper, reactivity.

2 a aluminium + iron oxide → iron + aluminium oxide

b The iron can be produced as a liquid just where it is needed. It runs down to join the rails together, filling the joint to make it strong.

3 a zinc + copper sulphate → copper + zinc sulphate
magnesium + zinc sulphate → zinc + magnesium sulphate

b magnesium > zinc > copper

4 a

Metal	Solution					
	scrittiby snerbide	splerbity snerbide	snibitty snerbide	stobbity snerbide	slibbity snerbide	blib snerbide
scrittiby	–	✗		✗	✓	✓
splerbity	✓	–	✓	✗	✓	✓
snibitty	✗		–	✗	✓	✓
stobbity	✓	✓	✓	–	✓	✓
slibbity	✗	✗	✗	✗	–	✗
blib	✗	✗	✗	✗	✓	–

b stobbity > splerbity > scrittiby & snibitty > blib > slibbity

c The reaction between scrittiby and snibitty snerbide or between snibitty and scrittiby snerbide should be done to decide whether snibitty or scrittiby is more reactive.

5 a $Mg(s) + ZnSO_4(aq) \rightarrow Zn(s) + MgSO_4(aq)$
$Mg(s) + CuSO_4(aq) \rightarrow Cu(s) + MgSO_4(aq)$
$Zn(s) + CuSO_4(aq) \rightarrow Cu(s) + ZnSO_4(aq)$

b Because they give a clear idea of whether one element is more reactive than another.

6 a A substance gains oxygen or loses electrons.

b A substance loses oxygen or gains electrons.

c A reaction in which both reduction and oxidation occur.

7 a Possibly zinc, copper. (Other possibles include tin and lead.)

b Redox reactions – the metals are reduced (lose oxygen) and the carbon is oxidised.

c These are noble metals and they are found in the pure state, not combined with other elements in an ore.

8 a i, ii and iv

b $Cu^{2+}(s) + H_2(g) \rightarrow Cu(s) + 2H^+(l)$
$Sn^{4+}(s) + 2Mg(s) \rightarrow Sn(s) + 2Mg^{2+}(s)$

19 Acids and alkalis

1 a Substances which change colour according to whether they are in acid, neutral or alkaline solutions are called indicators.

   b When a substance dissolves in water it forms a solution which may be acidic, neutral or alkaline.

   c The pH scale is used to show how acidic or alkaline a solution is.

   d When non-metal oxides dissolve in water their solutions are acidic, with a pH less than 7.

   e When metal oxides dissolve in water their solutions are alkaline, with a pH greater than 7.

2 The correct symbol is the one showing the hand and the flat surface, with two test tubes dripping corrosive liquid onto them.

3 Approximate pH values as follows

   a 5   b 7   c 14   d 0   e 10

   f A strong acid ionises completely in solution in water e.g. sulphuric acid, hydrochloric acid, nitric acid etc. A weak acid is only partly ionised in solution e.g. ethanoic acid, carbonic acid.

4 a

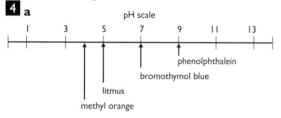

   b methyl orange

   c phenolphthalein

   d bromothymol blue

20 Metals and acids

1 Bubbles of gas, hydrogen, smaller, dissolves, reactive.

2 a All acids are substances which contain hydrogen.

   b When an acid is dissolved in water it forms hydrogen ions, H^+.

   c When an alkali dissolves in water it forms hydroxide ions, OH^-.

   d When an acidic solution reacts with an alkaline solution H^+ and OH^- ions combine to form water.

   e An acid reacting with an alkali is called neutralisation.

3 Test with a lighted splint – if it pops the gas is hydrogen.

4 a An acid is a proton (hydrogen ion) donor.

   b A base is a proton (hydrogen ion) acceptor.

   c A soluble base.

   d A substance in which the hydrogen found in an acid is replaced, directly or indirectly, by a metal.

5 a B   b A   c B > C > A

   d This involves control of all variables except the independent variable and the dependent variable, which form the basis of the investigation. In this case the independent variable is the metal, and the dependent variable is the rate at which hydrogen

gas is given off. Students should therefore suggest controlling all other variables (such as temperature of the acid and its concentration, cleanness of the metal surface etc) for the test to be 'fair'.

6 a Students should describe the investigation in terms of measuring the rate at which bubbles of gas are evolved from the surface of the metal, as described in the Student's Book. They should ensure that variables such as acid concentration and temperature are controlled.

   b copper + hydrochloric acid – no reaction as copper is below hydrogen in the reactivity series.

magnesium + hydrochloric acid → magnesium chloride + hydrogen

$Mg + 2HCl \rightarrow MgCl_2 + H_2$

zinc + hydrochloric acid → zinc chloride + hydrogen

$Zn + 2HCl \rightarrow ZnCl_2 + H_2$

21 Neutralisation

1 Neutralisation, salt, metal, indigestion.

2 Bee stings are acid, wasps stings are alkaline.

3 a Sulphur dioxide reacts with oxygen and water in the atmosphere to form sulphuric acid.

   b Chalk reacts with the acid and helps to neutralise it.

   c Sodium hydroxide is too strong an alkali.

4 zinc oxide + hydrochloric acid → zinc chloride + water

magnesium oxide + sulphuric acid → magnesium sulphate + water

copper carbonate + nitric acid → copper nitrate + water + carbon dioxide

sodium carbonate + ethanoic acid → sodium ethanoate + water + carbon dioxide

5 a metal oxide + acid → salt + water, any appropriate example

   b metal hydroxide + acid → salt + water, any appropriate example

6 a sulphuric acid + potassium hydroxide → potassium sulphate + water

$H_2SO_4(aq) + 2KOH(aq) \rightarrow K_2SO_4(aq) + 2H_2O$

   b hydrochloric acid + lithium hydroxide → lithium chloride + water

$HCl(aq) + LiOH(aq) \rightarrow LiCl(aq) + H_2O$

   c nitric acid + sodium hydroxide → sodium nitrate + water

$HNO_3(aq) + NaOH(aq) \rightarrow NaNO_3(aq) + H_2O$

22 Salt formation

1 The following steps are required. Put a measured amount (about 50 cm³) of sulphuric acid in the conical flask. Add copper oxide slowly, stirring with the stirring rod. The solution will turn blue as copper sulphate is formed. Keep adding copper oxide until no more will dissolve. Black copper oxide will then make the solution dark and cloudy. Filter the solution into the evaporating basin to remove the solid copper oxide. Evaporate off the water.

2 a Because it reacts with the limescale and dissolves it.

b sodium hydrogen sulphate + calcium carbonate →
sodium sulphate + calcium sulphate + carbon dioxide + water

Alternatives:
sodium sulphate + sulphuric acid + calcium carbonate →
sodium sulphate + calcium sulphate + carbon dioxide + water

or sulphuric acid + calcium carbonate →
calcium sulphate + carbon dioxide + water

c The ions remain trapped in the solid so they cannot react. With water present, the ions can dissolve so that they are mobile.

3 Beakers 1a and 1b: H^+ and OH^- react.
Beakers 2a and 2b: H^+ and CO_3^{2-} react.
Beakers 3a and 3b: H^+ and HCO_3^- react.

4 a Any suitable combination can be used here as long as the experimental details are accurate and due awareness of safety procedures shown.

b You can tell when the reaction is completed because the solid reactant builds up.

c They have to be removed by filtration.

5 a Nitrates and ethanoates, all sodium, potassium and ammonium compounds

b Carbonates and hydroxides

c i $Fe_2O_3(s) + 6HCl(aq) \rightarrow 2FeCl_3(aq) + 3H_2O(l)$
ii $Cu(OH)_2(s) + 2HNO_3(aq) \rightarrow Cu(NO_3)_2(aq) + 2H_2O(l)$

6 a Reacting an acid with an excess of a suitable salt, using a titration, using a precipitation reaction, by direct combination.

b In each case, marks given for choice of suitable salt, for correct procedure and safety awareness – see chapter 11 in Student's Book for detail of techniques.

7 $H^+(aq) + OH^-(aq) \rightarrow H_2O(l)$
$2H^+(aq) + CO_3^{2-}(aq) \rightarrow H_2O(l) + CO_2(g)$
$H^+(aq) + HCO_3^{2-}(aq) \rightarrow H_2O(l) + CO_2(g)$

8 The white powder is the anhydrous salt – without water – there is no water bound up with the salt. If crystals form slowly, water molecules become part of the crystal structure. This is known as 'water of crystallisation' and the salt is hydrated. You can calculate the amount of water of crystallisation by measuring the hydrated compound, heating it until it is anhydrous and weighing again. The difference is the water of crystallisation.

23 Titration calculations

1 Answer must include:
- careful filling of burette using funnel, adjusting level, careful initial readings, take meniscus into account.
- use of pipette to transfer known amount of other reactant into conical flask

- choice of suitable indicator
- white tile/paper to make colour changes clearer
- careful use of burette adding reactant dropwise as end point approaches
- accurate final reading from burette
- repeat process three times and find average result.

2 a The formula mass in grams of sodium hydroxide is $(23 + 16 + 1) = 40$, so one mole of sodium hydroxide has a mass of 40 g. So 1 dm^3 of solution which contains 40 g of NaOH is 1 mol dm^{-3}, or 1 M.

b Find out how much sodium hydroxide is present in 1 cm^3 of solution:
if 40 g of sodium hydroxide are dissolved in 500 cm^3 water then $\dfrac{40}{500}$ g of sodium hydroxide would be dissolved in 1 cm^3 of solution.
This means that $\dfrac{40}{500}$ g × 1000 g of sodium hydroxide would be dissolved in 1000 cm^3 of solution
= 40 g × 2 = 80 g of sodium hydroxide would be dissolved in 1000 cm^3 of solution.
80 g of sodium hydroxide is $\dfrac{80}{40}$ moles = 2 moles.
So the concentration of the solution is 2 mol dm^{-3} or 2 M.

3 The equation for this reaction is
$NaOH(aq) + HCl(aq) \rightarrow NaCl(aq) + H_2O(l)$
This tells us that 1 mole of NaOH is neutralised by 1 mole of HCl.
The number of moles of acid added to the sodium hydroxide solution can be calculated as follows:
The concentration of the HCl is 0.50 mol dm^{-3}, so 0.50 moles of HCl are dissolved in 1000 cm^3 of acid and $\dfrac{0.50}{1000}$ moles of HCl are dissolved in 1 cm^3 of acid
therefore $\dfrac{0.50 \times 20.0}{1000}$ moles of HCl are dissolved in
20.0 cm^3 of acid = 0.010 moles of HCl dissolved in 20.0 cm^3 of acid
The equation for the reaction tells us that 0.010 moles of HCl will exactly neutralise 0.010 moles of NaOH. This means that there must have been 0.010 moles of NaOH in the 25.0 cm^3 of solution in the conical flask.
0.010 moles of NaOH are dissolved in 25.0 cm^3 of solution.
Therefore $\dfrac{0.010}{25}$ moles of NaOH are dissolved in 1 cm^3 of solution.
So there are $\dfrac{0.010 \times 1000}{25}$ moles of NaOH in 1000 cm^3 solution = 0.40 moles of NaOH in 1000 cm^3 solution.
So the concentration of the sodium hydroxide solution is 0.40 mol dm^{-3} (0.40 M).

4 a $HCl + NaOH \rightarrow NaCl + H_2O$

b The concentration of the HCl is 0.10 mol dm⁻³, so 0.10 moles of HCl are dissolved in 1000 cm³ of acid and $\dfrac{0.10}{1000}$ moles of HCl are dissolved in 1 cm³ of acid

therefore $\dfrac{0.10}{1000} \times 15.0$ moles of HCl are dissolved in 15.0 cm³ of acid = 0.0015 moles of HCl are dissolved in 15.0 cm³ of acid.

c The equation for the reaction tells us that 0.0015 moles of HCl will exactly neutralise 0.0015 moles of NaOH. This means that there must have been 0.0015 moles of NaOH in the 25.0 cm³ of solution in the conical flask.

d 0.0015 moles of NaOH are dissolved in 10.0 cm³ of solution

Therefore $\dfrac{0.0015}{10}$ moles of NaOH are dissolved in 1 cm³ of solution.

So there are $\dfrac{0.0015 \times 1000}{10}$ moles of NaOH in 1000 cm³ solution = 0.15 moles of NaOH in 1 dm³ solution.

5 a $CH_3COOH(aq) + NaOH(aq) \rightarrow$ $NaCH_3COO(aq) + H_2O(l)$

b 0.50 moles of NaOH are dissolved in 1000 cm³ of acid

So $\dfrac{0.5}{1000} \times 25$ moles of NaOH in sodium hydroxide solution added to vinegar = 0.0125 moles NaOH.

c 1 mole of ethanoic acid reacts with 1 mole of sodium hydroxide so if there are 0.0125 moles of sodium hydroxide there will be 0.0125 moles of ethanoic acid.

d 0.0125 moles in 20 cm³ ethanoic acid

So $\dfrac{0.0125 \times 1000}{20}$ moles in 1000 cm³ ethanoic acid.

Concentration of ethanoic acid is 0.625 mol dm⁻³.

6 a Clear and precise description of a titration.

b 0.2 mol dm⁻³ potassium hydroxide means there is 0.2 mole KOH in 1000 cm³ water.

$\dfrac{0.2}{1000}$ moles KOH in 1 cm³ water

So $\dfrac{0.2}{1000} \times 34.0$ moles = 0.0068 moles of potassium hydroxide were needed to neutralise the acid.

c The equation shows that 2 moles of potassium hydroxide reaction with 1 mole of sulphuric acid so: 0.0068 moles of potassium hydroxide react with 0.0034 moles of sulphuric acid

0.0034 moles in 25 cm³ sulphuric acid

$\dfrac{0.0034 \times 1000}{25}$ moles of sulphuric acid in 1000 cm³ solution

0.136 moles of sulphuric acid in 1000 cm³

So the concentration is 0.136 mol dm⁻³.

7 a Methyl orange

b $Na_2CO_3(aq) + 2HCl(aq) \rightarrow 2NaCl(aq) +$ $CO_2(g) + H_2O(l)$

c 17.5 cm³ 1 mol dm⁻³ HCl

1 mole in 1000 cm³ HCl

So $\dfrac{1}{1000}$ moles in 1 cm³ HCl

So number of moles of HCl which reacted with the sodium carbonate is

$\dfrac{1}{1000} \times 17.5 = 0.0175$ moles.

d 2 moles of hydrochloric acid react with every 1 mole of sodium carbonate so the number of moles of sodium carbonate is $\dfrac{0.0175}{2} =$ 0.00875 moles sodium carbonate.

e 1 mole of sodium carbonate weighs 106 g so 0.00875 moles weighs 0.928 g.

f 2.5 − 0.928 = 1.572 g

g Mass of 1 mole of water = 18 g

$\dfrac{1.572}{18} = 0.0873$ moles

h There are 0.00875 moles of sodium carbonate and 0.0873 moles of water. There are approximately 10 times as many moles of water as there are sodium carbonate, so $x = 10$ and the formula is $Na_2CO_3.10H_2O$.

24 Rates of reaction

1 Slow reactions: rusting of metal, silver tarnishing, oil forming.

Fast reactions: fireworks going off, an explosion, coal burning.

2 a Gas was produced during the reaction and as it was lost the mass decreased.

b The time taken for the reaction to take place.

c So that none of the liquid is lost when the reaction fizzes, as this would make a difference to the readings.

3 a One of the products (carbon dioxide) is a gas and so is given off as the reaction continues, causing a loss of mass.

b A: there are plenty of reactants and so the reaction is happening really quickly.
B: the rate slows down as the reactants get used up.
C: when all the reactants have been used up no more products can be formed and the reaction stops.

4 a Line graph correctly drawn.

b 0.2 g **c** 80 seconds

d 0.2/80 = 0.0025 g/second
= 0.15 g/min

25 What affects chemical reactions?

1 Area, smaller, concentration, pressure, double.

2 a The small sticks have a bigger surface area available to react than a large log and so they catch fire quicker.

b Cooling slows down reactions, including those which make food go bad. The temperature is lower in a freezer than in a fridge so the reactions in it are slower and food goes bad much more slowly.

c The concentration of oxygen is much higher in the gas jar than in the air, so there is more oxygen available to react and the reaction goes faster.

d A tablet has a small surface area and needs to dissolve before it can be absorbed into the body. A soluble painkiller is already dissolved before it is swallowed and so can be absorbed and start working much faster.

3 This must be marked on merit. Explanations should include ideas about the effect of particle size on the rate of reaction, that an explosion in a sawmill is simply many tiny particles of wood burning very rapidly in air and that such explosions only occur if there is a spark or flame which supplies the heat needed to start the reaction.

4 a Line graph correctly drawn.

b As the temperature goes up, it takes less time for the cross to disappear.

c As the temperature goes up, the rate of the reaction goes up – it goes faster.

d An increase in temperature makes the reacting particles move about faster, so they are more likely to collide. They also have more energy so collisions are more likely to result in reactions. This is why an increase in temperature increases the rate of a reaction.

5 a The smaller the size the faster the rate of reaction. The surface area available for reaction is much larger – more particles are exposed and available for collisions.

b Increasing the concentration of the reactants speeds up the reaction. The increased concentration increases the chances of the particles hitting each other.

c Increasing the temperature increases the rate of the reaction because particles are moving faster so they hit each other more often. More importantly, they are more likely to collide with enough energy to react.

26 Catalysts and enzymes

1 a An enzyme is a biological catalyst.

b The activation energy is the minimum amount of energy particles must have to react.

c A catalyst is a substance that can speed up the rate of a chemical reaction.

d Chemical reactions can only happen when reacting particles collide with one another.

e Concentration, surface area and temperature can all affect the rate of a chemical reaction.

2 Rate, faster, lower, affected, metals, enzymes, protein.

3 Catalysts increase the rate of a reaction. So does increasing the surface area. The holes in these catalyst pellets increase the surface area of catalyst available to

come into contact with the reacting substances, and so it increases the rate of the reaction even more.

4 a

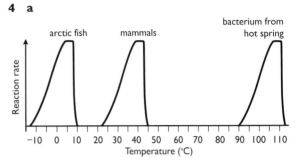

b The enzymes increase the rate of reaction up to their optimum (ideal) temperature. For each enzyme this is about the temperature they are usually exposed to. If the temperature goes up much above that optimum temperature the protein structure of the enzyme is destroyed and it no longer works.

27 Activation energy

1 a More particles are likely to collide with sufficient energy to react.

b Particles have to collide with a lot of energy to react. Relatively few of them will have a lot of energy and so the reaction rate is slower.

2 a

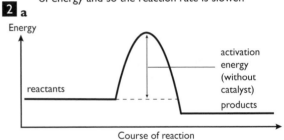

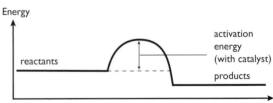

b A catalyst lowers the activation energy of a reaction, so that the particles do not need to collide with so much energy to react successfully. This means more collisions will successfully result in a reaction and so the rate of the reaction goes up.

3 a Lower the activation energy required for the reaction to take place.

b To give the largest possible surface area for reactions to take place.

28 Energy changes in reactions

1 **a** Chemists describe chemical reactions using equations.

b Chemical reactions need energy to be supplied before they will happen.

c Energy can be supplied in the form of heat or electricity to make chemical reactions happen.

2 **a** Graph A shows an exothermic reaction – the temperature goes up as energy is transferred form the chemicals to the surroundings.

b Graph B shows an endothermic reaction – the temperature drops as energy is transferred from the surroundings to the reacting chemicals.

c **i** exothermic   **ii** endothermic
iii exothermic   **iv** exothermic
v endothermic

3 There are a number of designs which pupils could come up with but all should involve measuring the temperature as the sherbet dissolves. Credit to be given for thought in planning, safety awareness and likelihood of the experiment providing a result.

4 **a** dynamite → carbon dioxide + nitrogen + water + oxygen

b Energy must be supplied to the dynamite before it will explode.

c Using a fuse which is lit (as seen on old films!).

d It produces large volumes of gas which literally blow everything around the dynamite apart.

5 **a** They get hot.

b The experiment might involve a 'coffee cup calorimeter' (two polystyrene cups, one inside the other) in which equal quantities of a strong acid and a strong alkali are mixed. A thermometer can be used to stir the mixture and to measure its temperature. Students might also suggest the use of suitable IT techniques here too, e.g. the use of a datalogger to plot the temperature rise and subsequent fall.

29 Calculating energy changes

1 **a** Before any reaction can take place the bond holding the atoms of the reacting substances together must be broken. Energy is supplied to break these bonds.

b Energy is released as new bonds form during a chemical reaction.

c **i** In an exothermic reaction more energy is released when the new bonds form than is taken in when the old bonds are broken. So there is an overall release of energy

ii In an endothermic reaction, more energy is taken in to break the old bonds than is released in the formation of new ones. So there is an overall uptake of energy.

2 **a** $\Delta H = -150$ kJ/mol; $\Delta H = +75$ kJ/mol

b $\Delta H = -75$ kJ/mol

3 **a** Exothermic, endothermic, endothermic, exothermic.

b It is endothermic and therefore needs an input of energy which is supplied by the sunlight.

c

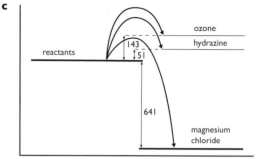

As there are no data, the relative sizes of the activation energies in the answer are unimportant.

4 **a**

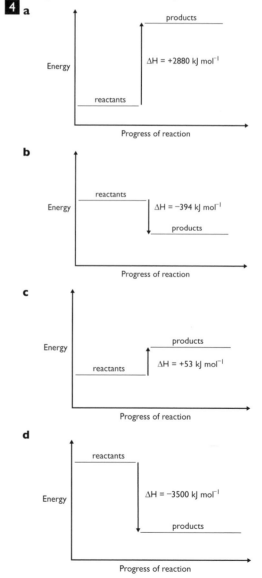

50

5 a The balanced equation for the reaction is
$H_2 + Cl_2 \rightarrow 2HCl$
This tells us that one mole of hydrogen molecules react with one mole of chlorine molecules to form two moles of hydrogen chloride molecules.
From the data table, the energy needed to break apart one mole of hydrogen molecules (H–H bonds) is 436 kJ/mole, and the energy needed to break apart one mole of chlorine molecules (Cl–Cl bonds) is 242 kJ/mole.
So the energy needed to break existing bonds in the reactants is 436 + 242 = + 678 kJ/mole.
The energy released in the formation of two moles of hydrogen chloride (H–Cl bonds) is
2 × –431 kJ/mole = –862 kJ/mole.
To find the overall energy change for the reaction combine the amount of energy taken in to break the bonds from the amount of energy released in bond formation.
Energy released during bond formation +
        energy taken in during bond breaking
= total energy transfer during the reaction
= –862 + 678 = –184 kJ/mole
or ΔH = –184 kJ/mole.

b The negative number shows that more energy was released in bond formation than was needed to break existing bonds, telling us that the reaction is exothermic

6 a The amount of energy needed to break one mole of a particular type of bond.

b Bond energy for breaking bonds is energy taken in and the measurement is positive; forming bonds energy is released so the measurement is negative.

7 a $H_2 + Br_2 \rightarrow 2HBr$ –103 kJ mol^{-1}
exothermic

b $C + 2H_2 \rightarrow CH_4$ –380 kJ mol^{-1}
exothermic

c $2CO + O_2 \rightarrow 2CO_2$ –322 kJ mol^{-1}
exothermic

d $N_2 + 3H_2 \rightarrow 2NH_3$ +1088 kJ mol^{-1}
endothermic

30 Industrial chemistry

1 a The main ingredient of any nitrate fertiliser is ammonia.

b Ammonia is made by the Haber process.

c The raw ingredients of the Haber process are nitrogen and hydrogen.

d The nitrogen comes from the air, the hydrogen comes from methane.

e Nitrogen is unreactive so the Haber process needs an iron catalyst.

f The process also uses a moderately high temperature and pressure.

2 A nitrogen and hydrogen   B 450 °C
C iron   D 200
E condenser   F liquid ammonia

3 a H_2SO_4

b Many uses, e.g. making fertilisers, manufacture of detergents and car battery acid.

c Solid sulphur heated → molten sulphur → molten sulphur mixed with dry air and oxidation takes place to give sulphur dioxide → sulphur dioxide mixed with air – reacts in presence of vanadium catalyst to give sulphur trioxide → sulphur trioxide mixed with concentrated sulphuric acid spray to form oleum → careful addition of water to give concentrated sulphuric acid.

4 At 27 °C, high yield of sulphur trioxide as the forward reaction is exothermic but reaction rate would be very slow. High pressure, increases yield of sulphur trioxide but very expensive to build high pressure plant and 97% yield can be obtained at normal pressures so not worth the expense.

5 a   **i** 20%   **ii** 45%   **iii** 70%

b 200 °C, 1000 atm

c It would be very expensive to maintain pressures of 1000 atm and very difficult and expensive to build and maintain an industrial plant which could stand those conditions.

d About 30%. This is the most economically sound set of conditions because although higher yields at lower temperatures the reaction would be very much slower.

31 The best conditions

1

Factor affecting rate of reaction	How it works
increasing the surface area of solid reactants	Makes more of the chemical available to react
increasing the concentration(liquids) or the pressure (gases)	makes particles more likely to collide as there are more of them closer together
increasing temperature	particles move faster, colliding more often and with more energy
use a catalyst	lowers activation energy or brings particles closer together

2 a $N_2 + 3H_2 \rightleftharpoons 2NH_3$

b 4   **c** 2

d Increases the yield of products on the right hand side where there is a smaller volume of gas.

e This is a compromise, as high as possible to increase yield without becoming prohibitively expensive in terms of plant or maintaining the pressure.

3 a Reversible reaction

b The reaction takes place at the same rate in both directions.

c Remove Z from reaction mixture as soon as it is formed.

4 a Catalyst

b Apparatus is open, so equilibrium is not set up.

c Damp pH paper turns blue.

d Burn it.

5 a In an ordinary reaction the reactants make products, e.g. $H_2 + Cl_2 \rightleftharpoons 2HCl$
In a reversible reaction as soon as the products are formed they react together again to reform the original reactants, e.g. $ICl + Cl_2 \rightleftharpoons ICl_3$
Iodine trichloride decomposes to give iodine monochloride and chlorine.

6 Amount of energy to make a bond is same as amount to break it – only difference is whether energy is absorbed (bond breaking) or given out (bond making). As the same bonds are made and broken in a reversible reaction, the amount of energy transferred is always the same.

7 a A system where matter cannot get in or out.

b It means they reach a point at which the reactions are going at exactly the same rate in each direction. Once this point is reached, the proportion of reactants and the products in the reacting mixture will remain the same.

8 a Temperature up, products down; temperature down, products up.

b Pressure up, products up; pressure down, products down.

c Reaction temperature up, products up; temperature down, products down.

32 Electrolysis

1 Current, conductors, electrolytes, electrolysis.

2 a A battery   B +   C –   D anode (positive)
E cathode (negative)   F solution

b i oxygen   **ii** hydrogen

3 bromine Br   calcium Ca^{2+} oxygen O^{2-}
hydrogen H^+ copper Cu^{2+} chlorine Cl^- lead Pb^{2+}
zinc Zn^{2+}

4

Solution	Cathode	Anode
copper chloride	copper	chlorine
zinc bromide	zinc	bromine
hydrochloric acid	hydrogen	chlorine

5 Anode: iodide, oxide, chloride, fluoride;
cathode: sodium, zinc, iron, aluminium, silver.

6 a $Cu^{2+}(aq) + 2e^- \rightarrow Cu(s)$

b Through the power supply.   **c** 31.75 g

33 More electrolysis

1 a A Positive sodium and hydrogen ions…
B Negative chlorine ions…
C Sodium hydroxide is left in solution.
D Sodium chloride ionises…

b $2Cl^-(aq) - 2e^- \rightarrow Cl_2 + 2H^+ + 2e^- \rightarrow H_2$

c Electricity

d

Product	Uses
hydrogen	making ammonia for fertilisers turning oil to fat chocolate
chlorine	killing germs in water making disinfectants making plastics such as PVC making bleach
sodium hydroxide	making bleach making soap making paper and ceramics cleaning ovens

2 a Careful description of process making clear that blue copper ions move through the acid to the negative electrode and the movement of the coloured ions through the acid can be seen. Also copper plating on electrode becomes visible. If the current is reversed the blue colour moves in the opposite direction and copper lost from electrode and plated onto the other one.

b Crystal of potassium manganate(VII) on damp filter paper and connected to a circuit. Purple colour spreads noticeably to the positive end. The negative purple manganate ions (MnO_4^-) are attracted to the positive electrode.

3 Electrolysis using impure tin as anode and pure tin as cathode, with a solution of a tin salt as the electrolyte.

4 a

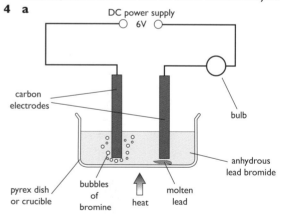

DC power supply
6V
carbon electrodes
bulb
anhydrous lead bromide
pyrex dish or crucible
bubbles of bromine
heat
molten lead

b Anode: $2Br^-(l) \rightarrow Br_2(g) + 2e^-$;
cathode: $Pb^{2+}(l) + 2e^- \rightarrow Pb(l)$

c Because at the anode the bromide ions lose electrons so they are oxidised, and at the cathode the lead ions gain electrons so they are reduced.

5 a A pinky orange copper coating
B greenish yellow gas (chlorine)
C electrolyte $CuCl_2(aq)$ D anode   E cathode

b At the cathode, copper ions from the solution gain electrons to form copper metal and coat the electrode. At the anode chloride ions from the solution lose electrons to form chlorine gas given off at the electrode.

c Electroplating metals.

34 Electrolysis calculations

1 **a** $2Na^+(l) + 2e^- \rightarrow 2Na(l); 2Cl^-(l) \rightarrow Cl_2(g) + 2e^-$

   b 17.75 g

2 **a** $CuBr_2$ **b** Cu^{2+}, Br^-

   c Cathode: $Cu^{2+} + 2e^- \rightarrow Cu$;
   anode: $2Br^- \rightarrow Br_2 + 2e^-$

3 **a** A unit which represents 1 mole of electrons.

   b A measure of a quantity of electricity – the amount of electricity which passes if 1 amp flows for 1 second,

   c 96 000

4 **a** $2Cl^- - 2e^- \rightarrow Cl_2$

   b $Cu^{2+} + 2e^- \rightarrow Cu$

   c $2O^{2-} - 4e^- \rightarrow O_2$

5 **a** Cathode: $Al^{3+} + 3e^- \rightarrow Al$;
   anode: $2O^{2-} - 4e^- \rightarrow O_2$

   b 48 g

6 **a**

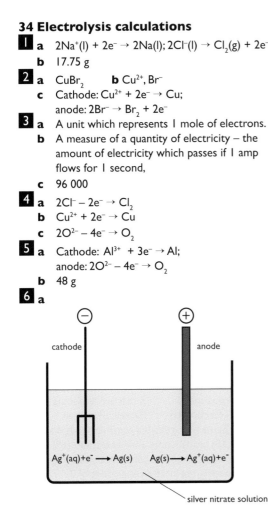

cathode   anode

$Ag^+(aq)+e^- \longrightarrow Ag(s)$ $Ag(s) \longrightarrow Ag^+(aq)+e^-$

silver nitrate solution

   b Cathode: $Ag^+ + e^- \rightarrow Ag$;
   anode: $Ag - e^- \rightarrow Ag^+$

7 The A_r of bromine is 80. Bromine molecules have the formula Br_2 so the M_r of bromine is $2 \times 80 = 160$. The number of moles of bromine molecules produced is $16/160 = 0.1$ moles. The balanced half equations tell us that for every mole of bromine molecules produced, one mole of copper atoms is produced, so if 0.1 moles of bromine molecules are produced, 0.1 moles of copper atoms are also produced. The A_r of copper is 63, so the mass of copper produced is $0.1 \times 63 = 6.3$ g.

8 The A_r of aluminium is 27, and 5.4 kg of aluminium is produced, which is 5 400 g.
The number of moles of aluminium atoms produced is
$\dfrac{5\,400}{27} = 200$ moles.

The balanced half equations tell us that for every 4 moles of aluminium atoms produced, 3 moles of oxygen molecules are produced. So if 200 moles of aluminium atoms are produced, this will produce:
$\dfrac{3}{4} \times 200 = 150$ moles of oxygen molecules.

The A_r of oxygen is 16. Oxygen molecules have the formula O_2, so the M_r of oxygen is 32. This means that the mass of oxygen produced is
$150 \times 32 = 4800$ g or 4.8 kg.

9 **a** Cathode: $2H^+ + 2e^- \rightarrow H_2(g)$;
   anode: $4OH^- - 4e^+ \rightarrow 2H_2O(l) + O_2(g)$

   b 1 faraday liberates 1 mole of H^+ ions which is 0.5 moles of H_2 molecules.
   So 0.03 faraday liberates $0.5 \times 0.03 = 0.015$ moles H_2.
   0.015 moles of H_2 occupies $0.015 \times 22.4 = 0.336$ dm^3 at stp.
   1 faraday liberates 0.5 mole of O^{2-} ions which is 0.25 moles of O_2 molecules.
   So 0.03 faraday liberates $0.25 \times 0.03 = 0.0075$ moles O_2.
   0.0075 moles of O_2 occupies $0.0075 \times 22.4 = 0.168$ dm^3 at stp.

   c 1 coulomb = 1 amp for 1 second
   96 000 coulombs = 1 amp for 96 000 seconds
   Or 2.5 amps for $\dfrac{96\,000}{2.5}$ seconds
   If a current of 2.5 amps was passed, 1 faraday would take $\dfrac{96\,000}{2.5}$ seconds So 0.03 faraday would take $\dfrac{96\,000}{2.5} \times 0.03 = 1152$ seconds
   (19.2 minutes).

35 Metal extraction

1 Earth, ore, concentrating, reducing, carbon/hydrogen, hydrogen/carbon.

2 Panning involves swirling a mixture of mineral and worthless rock around in water. The unwanted material is washed out of the pan, leaving the wanted mineral behind.

3 **a** zinc sulphide + oxygen $\rightarrow$ zinc oxide + sulphur dioxide

   b **i** Carbon must be used, as zinc is above hydrogen in the reactivity series.

   ii zinc oxide + carbon $\rightarrow$ zinc + carbon dioxide

4 Aluminium is found in the ore bauxite. Aluminium is extracted by electrolysis, since it is above carbon in the reactivity series. The bauxite is dissolved in cryolite and is heated to almost 1000 °C. A current passes through carbon electrodes into the molten mixture. Aluminium metal is formed at the cathode. Oxygen forms at the other electrode, reacting with it to form carbon dioxide.

5 **a** These would melt.   **b** Iron or titanium

6 **a** Potassium, sodium, calcium, magnesium, aluminium, reasons relating to reactivity series.

   b Silver, gold, platinum, reasons relating to reactivity series.

7 The arguments for recycling aluminium are based on the large amounts of energy needed to extract the metal from its ore.

8 a i $2O^{2-} \rightarrow O_2 + 2e^-$ ii $Al^{3+} + 3e^- \rightarrow Al$

b

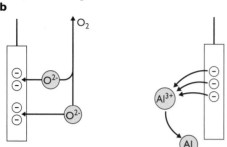

c i Oxidation (loss of electrons) occurs at the anode.

ii Reduction (gain of electrons) occurs at the cathode.

36 The blast furnace

1 Iron ore is a type of iron oxide. The reducing agent which is used to remove oxygen from iron oxide is carbon, in the form of coke. Coke and iron ore are mixed together and fed into a blast furnace, together with limestone. In the blast furnace, coke burns in a stream of hot air, and produces a gas called carbon dioxide. Carbon dioxide reacts with more carbon to form another gas, called carbon monoxide. Carbon monoxide reduces the iron oxide to iron. Molten iron runs to the bottom of the blast furnace, where it can be tapped off. The limestone reacts with acidic impurities to form a molten slag. The slag runs to the bottom of the furnace, where it floats on top of the molten iron.

2 A mixture of iron ore, coke and limestone
B hot gases out C blast of hot air in
D molten slag E molten iron F $1500\,°C$

3 a $C + O_2 \rightarrow CO_2$
b $C + CO_2 \rightarrow 2CO$
c $Fe_2O_3 + 3CO \rightarrow 2Fe + 3CO_2$
d $CaCO_3 \rightarrow CaO + CO_2$
e $CaO + SiO_2 \rightarrow CaSiO_3$

37 More metals

1 a Iron/steel reacts with oxygen and water in the air to form rust.

b The paintwork protects the metal from air and water and so prevents rusting. Once the paintwork is scratched, the air and water can come into contact with the metal and so rusting begins.

2 a Covers iron/steel and prevents contact with air.

b Tin is lower in the reactivity series than zinc so will not act as sacrificial anode if scratched.

3 a Appropriately drawn and labelled bar chart.

b Steel 1, 98.23%; steel 2, 97.56%.

4 a Data suitably displayed to compare steels.

b Silicon, carbon and manganese – only components which have changed.

5 Electrolysis – suitable diagram with kettle as cathode, copper anode and copper salt as electrolyte.

6 a 85%

b Electrolyte: zinc sulphate prepared from zinc oxide from the ore.
zinc oxide + sulphuric acid $\rightarrow$ zinc sulphate + water
Anode, lead; cathode, aluminium.
Zinc builds up on cathode
$Zn^{2+}(aq) + 2e^- \rightarrow Zn(s)$

c Thermal extraction. Zinc oxide heated with carbon in the form of coke in a furnace.
zinc oxide + carbon $\rightarrow$ zinc + carbon monoxide
zinc oxide + carbon monoxide $\rightarrow$ zinc + carbon dioxide

d Galvanising steel, alloys

7 a A spectacular exothermic reaction between chromium oxide and aluminium.

b chromium oxide + aluminium $\rightarrow$ chromium + aluminium oxide

c To coat other metals as it is resistant to corrosion.

38 Ordering elements

1 Elements, repeating, different, similar.

2 a Ne, unreactive gas   Na, very reactive metal
Si, solid non-metal   S, reactive non-metal
Cl, very reactive gas   Ca, reactive metal

b Boron (5) is a non-metal but aluminium (13) is a metal.

c Argon (18) would come after potassium (19).

d The inert gases had not been discovered then – this pattern repeated after a count of 7.

3 a He   C   F   Mg   S   Ca

b i Very reactive metals.
ii Very reactive non-metals (gases).
iii Unreactive gases.

c i Sodium   ii Potassium

4

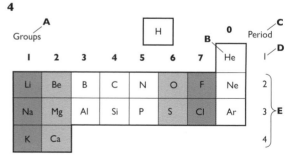

39 The Periodic Table

1 a Correctly plotted line graph. **b** 12

2 a Group 0 (noble gases)   **b** Non-metals

c Very very low **d** Group 4

e Non-metals **f** Very high

3 a Group 1   **b** Metals

c Correctly plotted line graph. Melting point gets lower.

d 40–50 °C. More reactive than potassium.

4 Unreactive, gases, atoms.

5 **a** Group 0 **b** 8 **c** Individual atoms

40 Metals

I Properties, air/water, water/air, ores, reactive, bases, salt.

2 Many examples are possible here. Three possible suggestions are shown.

Metal	Why and where used
copper aluminium steel	electrical wiring - good electrical conductor saucepans - good conductor of heat washing machine cabinet - strong, easily shaped, cheap

3 **a** Iron can be separated from other metals using a magnet.

b Choosing the right metal for a job involves finding out its properties and its cost.

c Metals can be mixed together to form alloys.

d Chromium can be added to iron forming stainless steel.

e The thermal conductivity of a metal measures how good it is at conducting heat.

4 **a** **i** tungsten **ii** sodium **iii** tungsten

b Mercury

c It has a very high melting point.

d **i** It has a low melting point, and so it is easily cast in moulds.

ii It is poisonous

e It will float as it is less dense than mercury.

41 Group 1 and 2 metals

I Alkali, reactive, shiny, electricity, soft, low.

2 **a** lithium + oxygen → lithium oxide

b **i** Fizzes steadily.

ii Melts and whizzes around.

iii Melts, whizzes around and gas catches fire.

3 **a** Turn purple/blue as a strong alkali is produced.

b Alkali metals – from this reaction.

c Hydrogen

d Lithium hydroxide

4 **a** Alkaline earth metals

b Dull grey metal – shiny when first cut but quickly forms oxide film.

5 **a** $CaO + 2HCL \rightarrow CaCl_2 + H_2O$
$Ca(OH)_2 + 2HCL \rightarrow CaCl_2 + 2H_2O$

b 74 g

6 The atoms get bigger down…
The bigger the atom, the further…
The further from the nucleus…
The weaker the force…
Alkali metals lose their outer…
Atoms with the 'looser' outer electrons…

42 Halogens

I Reactive, halogens, molecules, ionic.

2

Element	Symbol	State	Colour
fluorine	F	gas	yellow/green
chlorine	Cl	gas	green
bromine	Br	liquid	brown
iodine	I	solid	purple

3 **a** Iodine **b** Chlorine
c Bromine **d** Fluorine
e Iodine

4

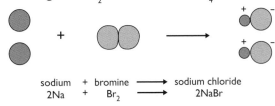

carbon + bromine → tetrabromomethane (carbon tetrabromide)

$C + 2Br_2 \rightarrow CBr_4$

sodium + bromine → sodium chloride
$2Na + Br_2 \rightarrow 2NaBr$

5 The atoms get smaller as you go up the group.
The smaller the atom, the closer…
The closer to the nucleus, the stronger…
Halogens have to gain an outer…
Smaller atoms towards the top…

43 More on halogens

I **a** Turn red, strong acid.

b Hydrochloric acid

c Hydrogen bromide

d Slower, Br is lower down Group 7 so it is less reactive.

2 **a** silver bromide $\xrightarrow{\text{light}}$ silver + bromine

b Photographic film contains…
In a camera, light falls…
Where light falls, the compound…
Where no light falls…
This produces a negative image…

3 **a** hydrogen + chlorine → hydrogen chloride

b Acid

4 a

Halogen	State at room temp.	Melting point °C	Boiling point °C	Appearance
fluorine	gas	−220	−188	yellow
chlorine	gas	−101	−35	green
bromine	liquid	−7	59	red/brown
iodine	solid	114	184	grey

  b Suitable graph of melting and boiling points.

  c Reactions with metals form an ionic bond – gain an electron to form negative ions. Reactions with non-metals form covalent bonds – share electrons to gain stable outer energy level.

5 a fluorine + hydrogen → hydrogen fluoride;
$F_2 + H_2 → 2HF$

  b iodine + hydrogen → hydrogen iodide;
$I_2 + H_2 → 2HI$

  c In **a** explosive under all conditions;
in **b** 300 °C + platinum catalyst, still slow and reversible.

6 a Chlorine more reactive than bromine or iodine.

  b **i** bromine + potassium iodide → iodine + potassium bromide
$Br_2 + 2KI → I_2 + 2KBr$

    ii chlorine + magnesium bromide → bromine + magnesium chloride
$Cl_2 + MgBr_2 → Br_2 + MgCl_2$

7 a **i** $AgNO_3 + KBr → AgBr + KNO_3$

    ii $AgNO_3 + NaI → AgI + NaNO_3$

  b Silver bromide and silver iodide insoluble in water so form as precipitates. Silver bromide is cream, silver iodide pale yellow, so adding silver nitrate to unknown solution means you can use colour of precipitate to identify the ions.

8 a Down group – less reactive. Atomic radius increases, so more energy levels screening positive attractive nucleus, so harder to attract electrons to fill outer level.

  b **i** $At_2 + H_2 → 2AtH$

    ii $At_2 + 2KI → At_2 + 2KI$ (no reaction as astatine is less reactive than iodine and so cannot displace it from KI)

44 Transition metals

1 Transition, heat, less, harder, melting, higher.

2 a iron   **b** zinc, nickel   **c** iron

3 a Transition metals.

  b All very similar metals.

  c A hard, magnetic metal with a high melting point, that forms coloured compounds.

4 a Very reactive   **b** Less reactive

  c Can float on water   **d** Sink in water

  e Low   **f** High

  g Colourless   **h** Often coloured

5 a Iron reacts slowly with water to form

hydrated iron oxide (rust) in the cold. It reacts with steam to form iron oxide and hydrogen. Copper reacts with oxygen in the air when it is heated to form copper oxide.

  b Copper only forms an oxide in strong heat so does not corrode easily and is used decoratively. Iron rusts, so needs protection from water by processes such as galvanising, painting or adding other elements to make steel.

  c Iron much more available and cheaper than copper so much more widely used.

6 a Sulphur dioxide (from burning fossil fuels) is present in these areas in greater concentrations than in other areas. This dissolves in rain to form sulphuric acid, which can react with the copper.

  b Carbon dioxide

  c copper + sulphuric acid + oxygen → green colour
copper + carbon dioxide + oxygen → green colour

7 a copper(II) oxide + sulphuric acid →
copper sulphate + water
$CuO(s) + H_2SO_4(aq) → CuSO_4(aq) + H_2O(l)$

  b copper(II) sulphate + ammonia solution →
copper hydroxide + more ammonia solution →
complex copper ion
$CuSO_4(aq) + NH_3(aq) → Cu(OH)_2 + NH_3(aq)$
$→ [Cu(H_2O)_2 (NH_3)_4]^{2+}$

  c Deep blue

45 Combustion

1 Nitrogen, oxygen, reacting, oxides, combustion.

2 a carbon + oxygen → carbon dioxide

  b Carbon dioxide gas, into the atmosphere.

3 a Water.

  b hydrogen + oxygen → water

4 a fuel + oxygen → waste gases + energy

  b Oxides

5 a Carbon dioxide and water.

  b oxygen + methane → carbon dioxide + water
$O_2 + CH_4 → CO_2 + H_2O$

6 a A Candle wax contains…
B The waste gases rise…
C The crushed ice cools…
D A colourless liquid condenses…
E The gas bubbles through…
F The limewater turns milky.

  b Water

7 Oxygen – you need a fuel plus oxygen for combustion.

8 a Oxygen.

  b The oxygen comes from the potassium nitrate.

  c Carbon dioxide and sulphur (di)oxide – oxides of carbon and sulphur.

46 Gases in the air

1 Sulphur, dioxide, rain, sulphuric, acidic, fish.

2 **a** Power plants
  b Nitrogen oxides and carbon monoxide.
  c Many cars there, so more pollution.
3 Air → carbon dioxide and water removed to prevent them blocking pipes when they become solid at low temps → remaining gases (oxygen, nitrogen and noble gases) pass through fine jet. As they expand from fine jet they are cooled further → cycle repeated until gases reach temp of −200 °C when the gases liquefy. Oxygen, nitrogen and noble gases separated from liquefied air by fractional distillation → nitrogen boils at around −196 °C and oxygen at around −183 °C. They can be collected and stored under pressure.
4 **a** Colourless, more dense than water, fairly → soluble in water, solid below −78 °C.
  b In fire extinguishers – it is a dense gas that puts out fires. In carbonated drinks.
  c Carbon dioxide reacts with soluble calcium hydroxide to form an insoluble compound (calcium carbonate) so the limewater turns cloudy with the white precipitate. This is used as a test for the presence of carbon dioxide. If carbon dioxide continues to bubble through the solution, the precipitate redissolves as it forms soluble calcium hydrogen carbonate.
  carbon dioxide + calcium hydroxide (limewater) → calcium carbonate + water
  $CO_2(g) + Ca(OH)_2(aq) → CaCO_3(s) + H_2O(l)$
5 **a** Correct diagram and labelling.
  b Ammonia is less dense than air so it rises and displaces the air.
  c Ammonia is a base so a change in the litmus will show that the tube is full of ammonia gas.

47 Analysis
1 **a** A way of identifying some of the metals in Groups 1 and 2 of the Periodic Table because, when they burn in air, they produce flames with a characteristic colour.
  b A small amount of the substance to be tested is placed in a wire loop and held in the hot flame of a Bunsen burner. The Bunsen flame then shows the colour of the metal element involved.
  c a red   b sodium
     c potassium   d orange-red
2 **a** potassium   **b** calcium
  c reddish brown precipitate
  d nothing observed   **e** aluminium
  f iron(II)   **g** nothing observed
  h golden yellow
3 Powder A is copper carbonate + explanations; powder B, can't identify with available tests; powder C – zinc carbonate + explanations; powder D, carbonate + explanation but can't tell which metal involved.
4 LiCl + explanation
5 $CuSO_4$ + explanation

6 **a** $NaNO_3$ **b** NH_3CO_3
  c fizzing – gas turns limewater milky
  d nothing observed   **e** nothing observed
  f brick red
7 **a** sodium bromide   **b** barium chloride
  c potassium iodide
8 **a** Ammonia is an alkaline gas that is readily soluble in water. NH_3.
  b Ammonia gas turns damp red litmus paper blue, since the gas dissolves in the water in the paper bringing it into close contact with the indicator. Ammonia is a pungent gas but damp red litmus paper will turn blue well before enough ammonia has been produced for the nose to detect it.
  Ammonium ions react with sodium hydroxide solution to form ammonia and water. Sodium hydroxide solution is added to a solution of the unknown substance. If ammonium ions are present, ammonia is formed. Gently warming the solution then drives off the ammonia as a gas, which can be detected using damp red litmus paper.
  $NH_4^+(aq) + OH^-(aq) → NH_3(aq) + H_2O(l)$
9 Detecting the presence of nitrate ions in an unknown substance makes use of the test for ammonia. Sodium hydroxide solution is added to a solution of the unknown substance and gently warmed. If no ammonia is detected, aluminium powder is added. The aluminium powder reduces any nitrate ions present to ammonium ions. These then react with the sodium hydroxide solution to form ammonia gas, which is given off and detected using damp red litmus paper.
  $3NO_3^-(aq) + 5OH^-(aq) + 2H_2O + 8Al →$
  $8AlO_2^-(aq) + 3NH_3(g)$

48 Crude oil
1 Hydrocarbons, molecules, atoms.
2 A Crude oil is heated…
  B The lighter, smaller particles…
  C Cold water cools the gas…
  D The liquid collects…
  E The beaker is changed…
3 **a** A petrol B paraffin (kerosene)
     C diesel D bitumen
  b Naphtha, fuel oil
4 **a** Line graph correctly drawn.
  b Boiling point goes up regularly.
  c 124 ± 4 °C
  d B – includes the boiling point of octane.

49 Organic chemistry
1 Organic – study of carbon compounds, inorganic – study of the remaining elements and their compounds
2 **a** The simplest family of hydrocarbons containing carbon atoms joined by single covalent

carbon–carbon bonds.

  b $CH_3—CH_2—CH_2—CH_2—CH_3$

  c They burn in air to give carbon dioxide and water.

  d Two from fuel for heat, as a form of lighting, heat for cooking, fuel for internal combustion engine (car, bus etc) or any other sensible suggestion.

  e $2C_4H_{10} + 13O_2 \rightarrow 8CO_2 + 10H_2O$

3 **a** Hydrocarbons that contain a carbon–carbon double bond.

  b $CH_3—CH_2= CH_2—CH_2—CH_3$ (double bond at any position)

  c Produced by catalytic cracking of alkanes.

  d Ethene reacts explosively so too dangerous; too valuable in the chemical industry in manufacture of plastics etc.

  e $C_4H_8 + 6O_2 \rightarrow 4CO_2 + 4H_2O$

4 **a** C_3H_8 $CH_3—CH_2—CH_3$

  b C_5H_{12} $CH_3—CH_2—CH_2—CH_2—CH_3$

  c C_8H_{18}
    $CH_3—CH_2—CH_2—CH_2— CH_2—CH_2—CH_2—CH_3$

5 **a** C_3H_6 $CH_3—CH_2=CH_3$ (double bond at either position)

  b C_5H_{10} $CH_3—CH_2=CH_2—CH_2—CH_3$ (double bond at any position)

  c C_8H_{16}
    $CH_3—CH_2—CH_2=CH_2—CH_2—CH_2—CH_2—CH_3$ (double bond at any position)

6 **a** 14   **b** 22   **c** 16   **d** 32

7 **a** 12   **b** 24   **c** 40   **d** 34

8 Butane burns more cleanly – lower carbon–hydrogen ratio, alkenes more useful in chemical industry because of double bond so not used as fuels.

9 **a** Bar chart drawn neatly and accurately with appropriate scale and labelled axes.

  b Boiling point depends on length of carbon chain – pentane has longest, each isomer has shorter carbon chain.

10 a Because the double bond is less than twice as strong as a single bond, so it is easier to break open one part of the double bond than to break open a single bond. This means less energy is needed for the reaction and so unsaturated molecules are more reactive.

  b Alkane – fully saturated, unreactive – bromine cannot displace the hydrogen atoms and so there is no reaction. Alkene – unsaturated so bromine is added across double bond – a bromoalkane is produced and bromine is removed from the bromine water making it colourless.

11 a Molecules which contain the same numbers of each type of atom but have different arrangements of atoms.

  b Check that all three are true isomers.

  c Check that all drawn are true isomers.

  d Correct name for each isomer drawn.

50 New products from crude oil

1 Hydrocarbon, cracking, temperatures, plastics.

2

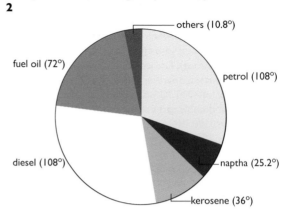

fuel oil (72°), others (10.8°), petrol (108°), naptha (25.2°), kerosene (36°), diesel (108°)

3 Alkanes, single, saturated, alkenes, double, unsaturated.

4 **a**

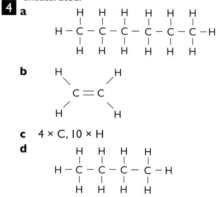

  c $4 \times C, 10 \times H$

5 **a** Because they are often mixtures of similar sized molecules, not a pure compound, and some of the molecules need further processing to be really useful.

  b Crude oil fraction containing larger hydrocarbons heated to vaporise hydrocarbons which are then passed over a hot catalyst which speeds up the process of thermal decomposition – the molecules break down to form smaller, more useful ones.

  c To form more reactive molecules with double bonds.

51 Polymers

1 **a** Any sensible answers, e.g. methane (cooking fuel), gasoline (petrol), kerosene (aviation fuel), diesel oil, domestic fuel oil.

  b Because oil is a fossil fuel and a finite resource – it will run out and so we need alternatives. Also fossil fuels produce high levels of carbon dioxide and alternatives that produce less carbon dioxide or use as much as they produce (carbon neutral) are being investigated.

2 **a** Long polymer chains with organic compounds as monomer units.

  b Any sensible answers, e.g. wide variety of properties and so uses; often very strong and do

not rot or corrode; can be shaped.
  c Different monomer units produce a different polymer with different properties.
3 Should show awareness of the problems and issues involved in the use of plastics and the need to look for viable alternatives and recycle, yet also recognise the usefulness of plastics in society.
4 **a** Big molecule – made up of very large numbers of different atoms combined. Polymer – made up of long chains of small monomer units joined together, at least 50 repeating monomer units for it to be called a polymer.
  b Because they are unsaturated and so have a reactive double bond which can be used to join the monomers together.
5 **a** When unsaturated monomers join together by the opening of the double bond and no other substance is produced in the reaction – it is simply an addition reaction between the two monomers.
  b In addition polymerisation nothing but the monomers is involved and nothing else is produced in the reaction. In some forms of polymerisation other molecules are produced – often water.
  c The carbon–carbon double bonds of the ethene molecules open up to form single bonds in the long chain of polythene.
6 **a** One bond on the double bond opens, leaving a free bond at each 'end' of the monomer. Adjacent monomers can then link up in a 'never-ending' polymer chain.
  b See diagram at bottom of page.

7

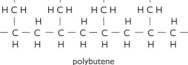

butene monomers

polybutene

52 Ethanol

I Intoxicating drink e.g. beer, wine; solvent e.g. perfume; fuel e.g. for cars.
2 In presence of oxygen yeast break down sugar completely to form carbon dioxide and water and no ethanol is formed.
3 Sugar, water and yeast mixed → warmed to 20–30 °C → yeast grows and enzymes break down sugar to ethanol in absence of oxygen → carbon dioxide allowed to escape → yeast removed by filtering → fractional distillation of ethanol/water mixture to extract pure ethanol.
4 **a** Butanol: C_4H_9OH, correct diagram; pentanol: $C_5H_{11}OH$, correct diagram.
  b

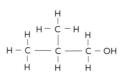

propanol: butanol:

5 General comments – as many advantages and disadvantages as possible, carefully argued – to include those in the book and any others which are thoughtful and well justified.
6 **a** To prevent oxidation.
  b Exposing wine to air.
7 **a** Propanol oxidised to propanoic acid.
  b Propanol $\xrightarrow{\text{oxidation}}$ propanoic acid
8 Molecular formula   propanoic acid C_2H_5COOH

   Structural formula

   Molecular formula   pentanoic acid $C_4H_9C\!\!\diagup^O_{OH}$

   Structural formula

Diagram for answer 6 b

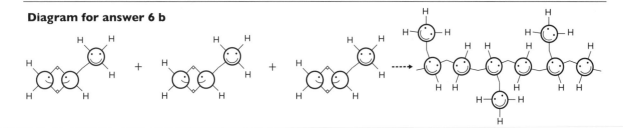

9 a Correct reaction to form ester and water,
whichever chosen.

b Concentrated sulphuric acid

c Food flavourings and perfumes

10 a

Method	Fermentation of plant material	Reactions of alkenes with steam
rate of reaction	relatively slow – several days per batch	rapid
quality of product	mixture – needs distillation	pure
use of resources	renewable resources (plants)	non-renewable resources (chemicals from oil)
batch or continuous	batch – but enough batches can make almost continuous production possible	continuous – more efficient
reaction conditions	low temperatures and ordinary pressures – very cheap to maintain	high temperatures and pressures – high energy input

b Well argued whichever chosen.

11

$$C_3H_7OH + C_2H_5COOH \longrightarrow C_5H_{12}COO + H_2O$$

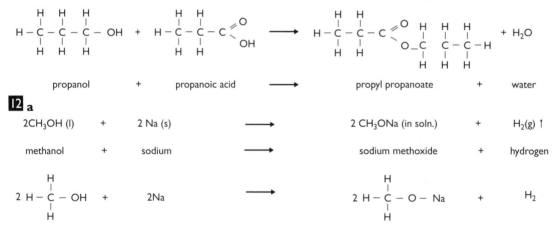

propanol + propanoic acid $\longrightarrow$ propyl propanoate + water

12 a

$$2CH_3OH (l) + 2\ Na\ (s) \longrightarrow 2\ CH_3ONa\ (in\ soln.) + H_2(g) \uparrow$$

methanol + sodium $\longrightarrow$ sodium methoxide + hydrogen

$$2\ H-\overset{\overset{\displaystyle H}{|}}{\underset{\underset{\displaystyle H}{|}}{C}}-OH + 2Na \longrightarrow 2\ H-\overset{\overset{\displaystyle H}{|}}{\underset{\underset{\displaystyle H}{|}}{C}}-O-Na + H_2$$

b Methanol, it has the shortest carbon chain.

Physics answers

1 Forces at work

1 Accelerate, speed, direction, distance, time, velocity.
2 a i Isuzu   ii Isuzu   iii Porsche
    iv Lada   v Porsche
   b Gemma is not right. Although the car with the largest engine (the Porsche) is the fastest, the car with the second largest engine (the Isuzu) has a slower top speed than most of the other cars.
   c i and ii

Manufacturer	Fuel used (gallons)	Cost of fuel
Audi	6.7	£23.33
BMW	4.3	£14.96
Citroen	6.0	£21.08
Ford	6.7	£23.33
Isuzu	10.4	£36.27
Lada	5.3	£18.67
Mazda	6.3	£21.88
Nissan	4.3	£15.12
Porsche	7.9	£27.78
Rover	4.9	£17.16

Fuel consumption is rounded to 1 d.p. but the cost has been calculated on exact fuel consumption.
   d Bar charts correctly drawn.
   e There is no simple relationship between these three ways of estimating the performance of a car. 'Performance' is quite a subtle thing to measure, since acceleration, top speed and power output are all measures of different things. More able pupils may point out that the weight of the car has not been taken into account in any of these measures. They might like to see whether they think that the power:weight ratio of the cars (found by dividing the cars' power output by its weight) provides any better measure of its 0–60 mph acceleration.

2 On the move

1 Fast, distance, constant, stationary, steeper.
2 a C; the distance increases steadily while the object is moving at a steady speed, and then the distance stops changing (the line on the graph is horizontal) when the object has stopped.
   b B; the graph is the steepest straight line.
   c D; the graph is the least steep straight line.
   d A; the graph is horizontal at first, showing that the distance is not changing, and then goes up as the object moves away.
3 a 10 m/s   b 3 m/s   c 200 m/s
   d 3.0 m/s
4 a The mouse is stationary for 2 s, then travels a distance of 6 m in the next 5 s, and a further 2 m in the following 3 s. It then remains stationary for 6 s.

   b 1.2 m/s   c   0.67 m/s
5 Graph correctly plotted with one line for each person.

3 Changing direction

1 a distance   b speed   c velocity
   d acceleration
2 a C; the graph is horizontal while moving at a steady speed, and then drops down to zero.
   b B; the horizontal line shows a steady speed, and the line is higher on B than on the other graphs.
   c D; the horizontal line shows a steady speed and the line is lower on D than on the other graphs.
   d A; the graph starts at zero velocity and then goes up.
3

Part of graph	Hamish's motion
0 to A	accelerates to a steady velocity of 2 m/s
A to B	walks at steady velocity of 2 m/s
B to C	slows down to a velocity of 1 m/s
C to D	walks at a steady speed of 1 m/s
D to E	slows down to a stop
E to F	stationary
F to G	accelerates to 5 m/s
G to H	runs at steady velocity of 5 m/s
H to J	slows down to a stop

4 a 2 m/s^2 b 6 m/s^2 c -3 m/s^2
   d -0.5 m/s^2 e 8 m/s^2
5 a Acceleration: $0A = 0.4 \text{ m/s}^2$, $AB = 0 \text{ m/s}^2$, $BC = -0.2 \text{ m/s}^2$, $CD = 0 \text{ m/s}^2$, $DE = -0.2 \text{ m/s}^2$, $EF = 0 \text{ m/s}^2$, $FG = 1 \text{ m/s}^2$, $GH = 0 \text{ m/s}^2$, $HJ = -1 \text{ m/s}^2$
   b 145 m

4 Changing motion

1 a To change an object's speed an unbalanced force must act on it.
   b A push or a pull is called a force.
   c When the forces acting on a body cancel out they are said to be balanced.
   d When an unbalanced force acts on an object in a particular direction the speed of the object changes (accelerates) in that direction.
   e The motion of an object is not affected by balanced forces acting on it.
   f The greater the size of an unbalanced force the faster an object will speed up or slow down.
2

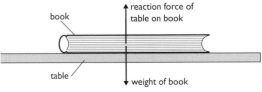

3

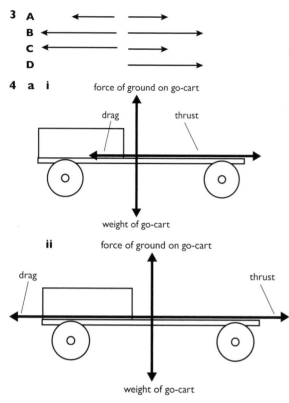

A
B
C
D

4 a i

force of ground on go-cart

drag

thrust

weight of go-cart

ii

force of ground on go-cart

drag

thrust

weight of go-cart

b The left hand go-cart will win, as the person pulling it can exert a much bigger force than the person pulling the other go-cart. This will make it accelerate more quickly.

5 Applying the brakes

I An object is moving, solid surfaces in contact with one another, is opposite to the direction in which the object is moving, in car brakes to slow down and stop moving cars, heat up and wear away.

2

Place	Size of frictional force	How is the frictional force controlled?
car engine	small	smooth metal surfaces which rub together in the engine
		oil circulated round engine over surfaces in contact
road surfaces	big	making the surface rough providing a way for water to drain away
sole of shoe	big	surface of sole is made rough

3 Dry runway - large frictional force between (non-rotating) tyre and runway leads to rapid heating of tyre and hence smoke. Wet runway - frictional force much smaller, so less heating and no smoke.

4 Although possible in principle, a drag chute would be impractical for airliners, as it would have to be

re-packed after each landing.

5 Text and diagrams should show how brakes are applied until wheel is about to lock, then released and applied again. This leads to a greater braking force than a locked wheel (shown with appropriate diagram).

6 Changing shape

I a A force can change the shape of an object.
b An object will return to its original shape and size when the force is removed if it is not deformed past its elastic limit.
c Extension is the amount something has stretched.
d When an object is stretched beyond its elastic limit it is permanently deformed.
e Energy transferred to an object beyond the elastic limit cannot be got back as useful work.

2 a y-axis extension   x-axis force
curve elastic limit
b When you stretch a spring by a small amount its extension is proportional to the force, and it goes back to its original length when the force is removed. If you stretch it too far, the spring passes its elastic limit. The extension is no longer proportional to the force, and it does not go back to its original length when the force is removed.
c Justin hung increasing masses on the spring and measured the amount the length of the spring increased (extension). Suitable diagram showing how the spring was mounted and how the extension was measured.

3 a Correctly plotted line graph.
b i 0.75 cm   **ii** 7.75 cm

4 Correctly plotted line graph with one line for each spring.
b Approximately 6.25 N (spring 1) or 3.75 N (spring 2)
c 14.5 cm

7 Driving around

I a i Thinking distance is the distance the vehicle travels in the time between the driver seeing something that means the brakes must be applied, and actually applying the brakes.
ii Braking distance is the distance the vehicle travels while the brakes are applied.
iii If you add the thinking distance to the braking distance you get the stopping distance.
b i Any two sensible answers e.g. the driver is tired, the driver has been drinking or has taken some types of drugs, the vehicle is travelling faster.
ii Any two sensible answers e.g. the road is wet, the road is icy, the vehicle's brakes have been badly maintained, the vehicle is travelling faster.

2 a 22, 54, 74
b A 'two-second gap' is safe for the first two speeds in the table, but at the higher speed it becomes too small.

c A bigger gap may be necessary when the road is slippery, such as when it is raining or when there is snow or ice.

3 a i

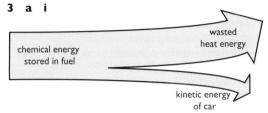

Students would not be expected to know the proportions of the energy transfers, but should appreciate that most of the energy in the fuel is transferred to heat energy.

ii

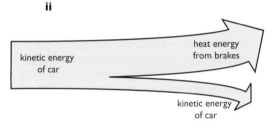

b All the energy will have been transferred as heat energy.

4 a 2250 N   **b** 1.5 m/s^2 **c** 600 kg

8 Keeping safe

1 Pressure, area, increases, stretch, limit.

2 Students should give explanations in terms of energy being absorbed by these objects as they are permanently deformed.

3 a A impact-absorbing bumpers, B crumple zone, C padding and collapsing steering wheel, D air bag, E sea tbelt, F steel cage.

b A range of possible ideas here, which may be quite imaginative. The ideas met so far provide possible solutions to the question 'How do you protect the passenger in the event of an impact?' Solutions will centre on minimising the pressure on the passenger's body through the use of padding, energy-absorbing parts of the car which deform permanently in an impact (like the crumple zones), and restraints which 'give' in an accident as the passenger is slowed to a halt.

4 The data in this graph clearly show that a seatbelt slows the car occupant down over a longer period of time (about 100 ms) than the time an unrestrained occupant spends slowing down (about 30 ms). As a result, much larger forces (about 8 000 N as opposed to 3 000 N) act on the unrestrained occupant, and this is likely to lead to serious injury.

9 Falling freely

1 a 20 N   **b** 7 500 N   **c** 450 N

2

	At Earth's surface	At Moon's surface	In deep space
mass	6000 kg	6000 kg	6000 kg
weight	60 000 N	10 000 N	0 N

3 Mass, gravitational, newtons, accelerates, frictional, terminal.

4 D, C, E, B, A

5 Along the lines of: When a person jumps out of an aeroplane, their *weight* makes them accelerate downwards. As they go faster, *frictional forces* (due to *air resistance*) increase. Eventually the frictional forces are the same size as the person's weight. At this point there is no unbalanced force acting on the person, so they travel at a steady speed - their *terminal velocity*. With an open parachute frictional forces are larger, so the person is not going so fast when the downwards force from gravity is balanced by the frictional force from the parachute. Their terminal velocity is smaller, so they hit the ground much more slowly when they are using a parachute than they would if they had no parachute.

10 Balancing

1 a anticlockwise   **b** clockwise
   c $F1 \times L1 = F2 \times L2$ **d** 62.5 N

2 200 N

3 500 Ncm or 5 Nm

4 550 N

5 It is easier to balance the ruler when it is flat on your finger, since a small movement of the ruler leaves its centre of gravity above the finger. However, with the ruler vertical, a small movement will move the centre of gravity sufficiently to topple the ruler.

6 Weight of shovel =50N
When the shovel is balanced with the fertiliser on one end, its centre of gravity is 10 cm to one side of the pivot, so the moment in that direction is 50N × 10 cm = 500 Ncm. The turning force from the fertiliser is:
weight × 20 cm =500 Ncm, so weight = 500/20 = 25 N
Mass of fertiliser = 2.5 Kg

11 Mains electricity

1 Batteries, direct, backwards, alternating.

2 A Flexible plastic case for insulation.
   B Copper wires to conduct electricity.
   C Colour coded for identification.
   D Twisted thin wires for flexibility.
   B, C and D can be in any order.

3 a A
   b 240 V – potential difference that drives the current (the working voltage).
   a.c. – alternating current.
   50 Hz – changes back and forth 50 times per second.
   c Batteries, or 'mains adaptor', power pack or equivalent.

d A – the higher the voltage, the better the insulation needed.

e A – high voltages are dangerous – earth wire for 'safety'.

f B – low voltage from batteries is safe, 240 V could kill, especially if wet.

4 **A** Wires correctly positioned.

   B Insulation cut back just enough…

   C Cable clamp secure.

   D Screws tightened.

   E Correct fuse fitted.

   Accept any suitably positioned labels.

5 Lots of bare wire showing. Screw missing from earth. Copper wire instead of fuse. Cable clamp loose. Cable clamp not over outer insulation. Nick in insulation visible outside plug. Live and earth wires connected to wrong terminals.

12 Electrical safety

1 Electricity, contract, heart, wet.

2 Live, live, live, will.

3 **A** Correctly wired.

   B Live current stops at the switch…

   C The rest of the wire is safe if touched.

   D Incorrectly wired.

   E The rest of the wire is live…

   F If you touch it, you will get a shock.

4 **A** Working current.

   B Fuse wire cold.

   C Overload.

   D Fuse wire heats up.

   E Fuse wire breaks, breaking the circuit.

5 **a** 13 A   **b** 2 A   **c** 5 A   **d** 5 A

   e 13 A   **f** 2 A

6 Normally the current in the live wire…

   If a fault occurs, some current escapes…

   The RCD detects that the current in the live…

   The RCD very quickly switches off the current.

13 Calculating electrical power

1 20 W

2 **a** **i** 2300   **ii** 57.5

   iii 60   **iv** 10

   v 0.5   **vi** 4

   vii 6   **viii** 24

   ix 230

   b **i, ii, ix** because 230 V

   c 13 A, 2 A, 2 A

   d i because largest power for heating.

   e ii 60 W is standard bulb wattage.

3 1080 J

4 **a** 3.0 V   **b** 0.2 A

14 Charges at work

1 Unlike charges attract. Like charges repel.

2 **A** An uncharged object has positive and…

B A charged comb has an excess of negative…

C The comb charge repels the negative…

D The remaining positive charges are attracted…

3 Stands on end, the same, like.

4 **a** The droplets are charged with the same charge so they repel and keep apart.

   b The thunderstorm induces a charge on your hair and like charges repel.

5 **A** As charge builds up on the dome…

   B Once the voltage is high enough…

   C Electric current is detected as electrons flow…

15 So what is electricity?

1 Electrically, attract, static.

2 All except fridge magnets, suction caps and mains electricity.

3 All substances carry both positive…

   These charges usually balance out.

   If you rub two substances together, negative…

   The one that gains extra negative charges…

   The one that loses some negative charges…

   Opposite charges attract one another.

   If enough charges build up, they can jump…

4 **a** Nylon.

   b Bar chart correctly drawn.

5 **A** Light falls on to a special charged material.

   B This leaves a negative image in the charge.

   C Dry ink powder is attracted to the charge.

   D The ink is transferred to paper.

6 Any charge that starts to collect on the trolley can be neutralised without sparking by electrons travelling along the chain.

16 What else is involved?

1 Insulators, electrons, conductors, current.

2 Generator – movement (kinetic); battery – chemical; microphone – sound; solar cell – light

3 **a** The bulbs have resistance, and so they heat up when a current flows through them.

   b Less. The bulbs are not as bright.

   c Decrease. Extra resistance in the circuit.

   d Brighter. Double the voltage to drive the current.

   e Bulbs go out. No current could flow.

4 **A** Short wire gives low resistance.

   B This gives a high current and bright light.

   C Long wire gives high resistance.

   D This gives a low current and dim light.

5 **a** **A** 1.5 V   **B** 3 V   **C** 0 V

   D 1.5 V   **E** 3 V

   b 8 cells

17 Circuit shorthand

1 Series, parallel.

2 **A** series   **B** series   **C** parallel

   D series   **E** parallel

3 **A** lamp   **B** cell   **C** switch (open)

   D resistor   **E** variable resistor   **F** ammeter

G voltmeter
4 **A** One cell and one bulb in series.
  B Two cells and one bulb in series with an open switch.
  C Two bulbs in parallel with two cells in series: two switches, one in each of the separate bulb loops.
  D A bulb, an ammeter and a cell in series with a voltmeter in parallel across the bulb.

5

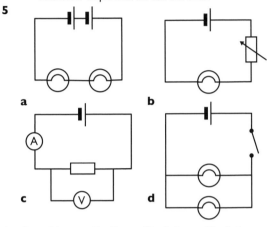

6 **A** neither **B** 2 **C** 1, 3 **D** 2, 3

18 Measuring electricity

1 Current, high, higher.
2 **a** Double the current. **b** Halve the current.
  c Current down to a tenth.
3 **a** The current gets bigger as the voltage gets bigger (directly proportional).
  b ~0.5 A **c** ~0.7 A **d** 1.2 A **e** ~11.7 V
  f 11.7 ohms
4 **a** 4.5 V **b** 0.5 A **c** 9 ohms **d** 1.5 V
  e 3 ohms – yes
5 **a** parallel **b** 0.5 A **c** 0.5 A **d** 6 V
  e 2 V
  f 4 V **g** smaller

19 Electricity by numbers 1

1 Resistor, diode.
2 **a**

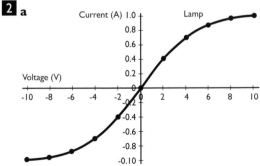

b

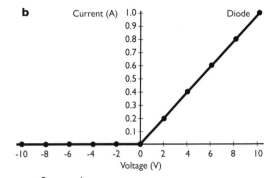

c See graphs.
d The increase in current starts to get smaller as the voltage increases. The resistance of the filament increases as the bulb gets hotter.
e No current flows if the connections are reversed.
f The current rises steadily with the voltage, like an ordinary resistor.
g 5 ohms
h 5.71, 6.9, 8.42, 10
i

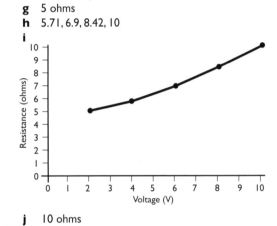

j 10 ohms
3 **a** 5 **b** 12 **c** 5500 **d** 220 **e** 0.25

20 Electricity by numbers 2

1 **a**

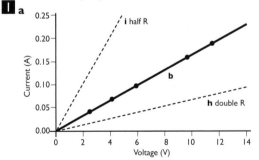

b See graph.
c Accurate – all very close to the line of best fit.
d 0.13 A
e 0.25 A
f No – it is beyond the range of experimental results (but not too far).
g resistance = 60 ohms
h, i See graph.

2 **a** 55 ohms
   b 25°C
   c 0.12 A
   d When the current drops close to/reaches 0.12 A.
   e When the current rises up close to/reaches 0.14 A.
   f

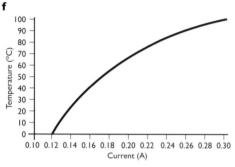

3 **a** Graph correctly drawn and plotted.
   b 6.0 V
   c That the graph can be extrapolated to a current of 100 A as it is a straight line.
   d Increased current drawn by starter motor decreases voltage of battery. This decreases current flowing through headlamp bulbs (by Ohm's law, I = V/R).

21 Waves – what are they?

1 **a** energy   **b** amplitude
   c wavelength   **d** frequency
2 **a** 0.4 m   **b** 1.6 m
3 **a**

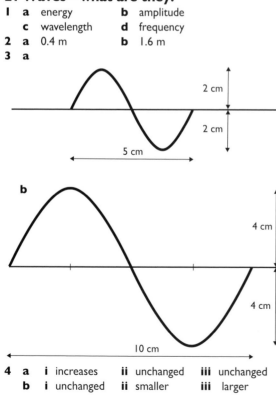

4 **a** **i** increases   **ii** unchanged   **iii** unchanged
   b **i** unchanged   **ii** smaller   **iii** larger

5 **a** A wave in which the vibrations move from side to side - at right angles to the direction of travel of the wave.
   b From side to side.
   c From side to side.

6 The ripples are transverse waves. The waves on the pond therefore move up and down and not from side to side, and the leaf moves in the same way.

22 Properties of waves

1 As waves enter shallow water they slow down. This refracts the waves towards the normal.
2 298 900 000 m/s
3 0.1 Hz
4 5 m
5 **a** 0.3 Hz   **b** water wave
   c 300 000 000 m/s   **d** radio wave
   e 2 m   **f** sound wave
6 **a**

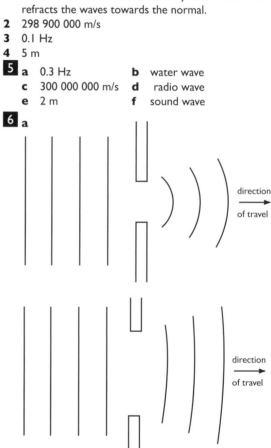

   b Diffraction

23 The radiation family

1 Electromagnetic, energy, waves, straight, speed.
2 **a** All electromagnetic radiations travel as waves. The electromagnetic radiations behave in similar ways.
   b All electromagnetic radiations travel at the same speed. Radio waves travel at the speed of light.
   c All electromagnetic radiations travel in straight lines. It is impossible to see round corners.
   d All electromagnetic radiations can travel through space. Infra-red radiation from the Sun can reach the Earth.
3 **a** 0.1 s   **b** 13 s   **c** 500 s
4 **A** infra-red   **B** light   **C** radio

D ultraviolet   **E** microwaves

5 9 500 000 000 000 km (9.5 million million km)

6 a 1.7 m

  b The calculation assumes that there is no delay between the gun firing and the signal travelling through the TV system. It also assumes that there are no delays in the TV transmitting system.

24 Using radiation

1 X-rays can be used to see inside a person's body. Radio waves have wavelengths longer than about 10 cm. Infra-red waves cook food under a grill. Light waves are visible to the eye. Gamma waves are given off by some radioactive substances. Ultraviolet waves help produce a sun tan. Microwaves cook food by transferring energy to water molecules.

2 The microwaves can cook people's skin and muscles in just the same way as they cook meat, by transferring energy to water molecules in whatever is being cooked.

3 People are generally warmer than their surroundings, so they emit more infra-red radiation than their surroundings. Thermal imaging equipment picks up this radiation and converts it to visible light, so that the person can be seen.

4 Brightening agents in the washing powder absorb ultraviolet radiation and emit it as visible light.

5 a i 30   **ii** 90   **iii** 225   **iv** 360

  b These figures are very variable since people's responses to ultraviolet radiation vary, the sunscreen may not be applied correctly, and the amount of ultraviolet radiation coming from the sun varies too, according to latitude. Surroundings also have an effect – more ultraviolet radiation will be absorbed on a beach than anywhere else, for example, because it is reflected from the sea and the light-coloured sand.

6 a The film is exposed and turns black where X-rays hit it, while it remains white where is not exposed. There is no exposure where the 'shadow' of a bone is cast, so these areas are white, while the rest is exposed to X-rays and so is black.

  b These will interfere with the X-radiogram, as they absorb X-rays and so will cast a shadow on the film.

  c X-rays can damage cells, and so exposure to them must be kept to a minimum consistent with the need to obtain a clear picture of what is happening inside the person.

25 Bending light I

1 change direction, speed, speed

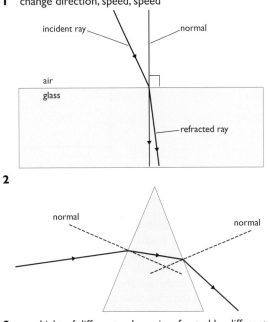

2

3 a Light of different colours is refracted by different amounts when it enters the glass. The different colours of light therefore follow slightly different paths through the prism, emerging at different points.

  b The top ray is red, the lower ray violet.

4 a The ray enters the glass at right-angles to it.

  b This happens because light bends away from the normal as it leaves the glass and enters the air.

  c Critical angle

  d Total internal reflection

  e 42°

5 a

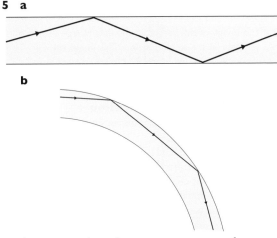

  b

Answers can show almost any arrangement of rays, as long as the angle of incidence in each case is equal to the angle of reflection.

6

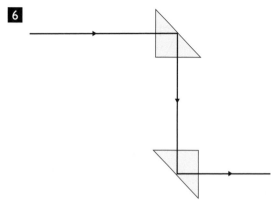

The two prisms must be arranged one above the other.

26 Bending light 2

1 Reflected, light, Sun, absorbed, darker.
2 The two reflected rays added to the diagram should each make the same angle with the normal as the incident ray with which they are paired.
3 Water is added to the cup. The light from the coin is then refracted, and it becomes visible.
4 The ray meets the wall of the fibre at an angle of incidence greater than the critical angle, so it is totally-internally reflected.

5

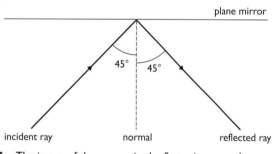

6 The image of the person in the first mirror produces an image in the second mirror. This image then produces an image in the first mirror, and so on …

7 a 1.32   b 49°

27 Sound and communication

1 Energy, vibrating, microphone, oscilloscope.
2 **A** low pitch and quiet   **B** high pitch and quiet
   C low pitch and loud
3 **a** Sound waves from the speaker's voice strike the base of the cup. This causes it to vibrate, which sends vibrations along the (taut) string. The string sets the base of the second cup vibrating, which sets up sound waves in the air. These enter the listener's ear, so that they hear the voice of the first person speaking.
   b The string will not vibrate if it is not tight.
   c This stops the vibrations passing this point.
   d Connect the strings of two telephones

together. Three people can then listen while one person talks.

4 330 m/s (to 2 sig.fig.)

5 a 4.4 s   b 3.4 s

6 Sound waves carrying the human voice have a wavelength of about 1 m, while light waves have a wavelength much smaller than this (about one millionth of a metre). So sound is diffracted round corners, while light is not. (A more complex explanation also takes into account that both sound and light can be reflected from hard surfaces. However, the reflected light will only produce an image if the reflecting surface is very flat, such as shiny metal, or a mirror. Otherwise the light rays are scattered widely. This is not so with sound waves, due to their much longer wavelength.)

28 Useful sounds

1 Echo, bats, echolocation, ultrasound, 20 000 Hz, hear.
2 **a** 150 m   **b** 0.067 s
   c The sound pulse is partly reflected from a shoal of fish 75 m below the boat, and from the sea bed 300 m below the boat.
3 Drawing should convey the idea that the sound wave is reflected round the gallery, bouncing off the wall until it reaches the listener's ear. Diagram should have incident and reflected paths of sound (roughly) equal.
4 333 m/s
5 250 m/s

29 What is energy?

1 Energy, light, sound, kinetic, electrical.
2 Moon – light.
   Catherine wheel – stored chemical/kinetic.
   Bonfire – stored chemical/heat/light.
   Boy/girl with walkman/headphones – stored chemical/electrical/sound – and torch – stored chemical/electrical/light.

3

Active energy	Stored energy
light	chemical
heat	potential
chemical	
electrical	

4 **a** chemical, heat   **b** mechanical, kinetic
   c chemical, electrical   **d** chemical, kinetic
   e mechanical, kinetic
5 **a** Microphone, sound, electrical; loudspeaker, electrical, sound
   b Motor, electrical, kinetic; generator, kinetic, electrical
   c Solar cell, light, electrical; light bulb, electrical, light
   d Up, kinetic, potential; down, potential, kinetic

30 Energy change efficiency

1 **a** Sankey diagrams showing: for electric fire 99% electrical energy converted to heat energy, 1% 'other';

for petrol engine 35% stored chemical energy converted to kinetic energy, 5% as sound, 60% 'waste' heat energy.

b　**i** 92% heat　　　**ii** 50% heat/sound
　　iii 10% heat　　　**iv** 30% heat/sound

c　**i** transformer > vacuum cleaner > food mixer > light bulb

　　ii Bar chart correctly drawn.

2 a 0.6　　　　　**b** 0.75　　　**c** 0.8

3 a 1000 J (1 KJ)　**b** 0.05　　　**c** heat energy
　d 1280 W　　　**e** 0.78

4 a 90 KJ, 910 KJ　**b** 950 KJ　**c** 446 500 J
　d 400 500 J　**e** 453 150 J

31 Heat energy on the move

I Conductors, poor, currents, convection, radiation.

2

Conductors	Insulators
copper	wood
aluminium	ice
silver	plastic
brass	glass

3 a Metal conducts heat energy to the food; plastic insulates the handles to stop you getting burnt.

　b The metal handles would conduct heat and get too hot to hold.

　c The cork is an insulator; it stops the heat energy damaging the table.

4 A The water is heated and expands.

　B The hot water floats up…

　C The water cools and contracts.

　D It sinks back down…

5 a 60 °C　　**b** 30 °C　　**c** 15 °C

　d The bigger the temperature difference between the coffee and the surroundings, the faster the energy will be lost.

　e 25°C, this must be room temperature, so no further heat energy is lost.

32 Stopping heat from moving

I energy, insulators, trapped, bubbles, fibres, radiation.

2 A Plastic or cork lid…

　B Vacuum to stop heat loss…

　C Hard case to protect the glass.

　D Hollow, double-layered glass bottle…

3 a 45°C　　　　　**b** 60°C

　c Glass B is insulated.　**d** 15°C

　e Zero or just a couple of degrees. They will both end up at room temperature; glass B just takes longer to get there.

4 a Graph correctly drawn with two curves on same axes.

　b B was silver. It radiates heat energy less well than the black can (can A), so it takes longer to cool down.

33 Heat transfer

I a Atoms have tiny charged particles…
　In metals, some of the electrons can…
　When a metal is heated, these electrons…
　These faster electrons spread out…
　The electrons collide with other particles…
　In this way energy is transferred…

b

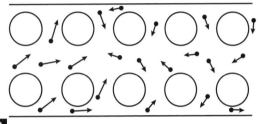

2 a Conduction and convection need particles of matter. The Sun is separated from us by empty space.

　b infra-red

　c White reflects the radiation, so the house stays cool inside.

　d To maximise the absorption of heat radiation energy.

　e The shiny aluminium is a poor radiator of heat energy.

3 a The heat energy enters the room as radiation through the window. Air cannot escape by convection as the window cannot be opened. Convection also causes heat from the rest of the house to be transferred to the attic.

　b The dry grass insulated Jacqui from the rocks, so the heat was not conducted away from her. The space blanket stopped heat loss by radiation and convection.

　c Because the space blanket reduced her heat radiation.

4 a The temperature will rise as this radiation carries energy into the greenhouse.

　b It will be reflected back into the greenhouse.

　c The greenhouse effectively traps energy. Energy carried by visible radiation (light) is able to pass into the greenhouse. A small amount of this is reflected back out (otherwise things in a greenhouse would be invisible from the outside) but much of it is absorbed. It is then re-radiated as infra-red radiation, which is unable to pass out back through the glass.

　d Just as the glass in a greenhouse allows energy in, but stops infra-red radiation travelling back out, greenhouse gases like carbon dioxide reduce the amount of infra-red radiation that can escape from the Earth back into space. Increasing amounts of fossil fuels have been burned in the last 50 years. This has caused the concentration of carbon dioxide in the atmosphere to rise. Many scientists suggest that this is enhancing the greenhouse effect. (Better-read pupils will recognise this argument as a great simplification, which is somewhat contentious.)

34 Energy in the home

1 Heating, fossil, continuous, expensive.
2 **a** Walls.
  b Area of windows is less than area of wall.
  c £75 **d** 2 years **e** £50
  f Probably not: 'window loss' is about £75 a year. It would take 30 years to pay this back if all the cost was saved, but at 'half savings' it would take 60 years.
3 **a** Fibreglass 15, mineral wool 17, cellulose 18, polystyrene 15, polyurethane 15, vermiculite 14.
  b Cellulose
  c Bar chart correctly drawn.
  d No. If not recycled, you would have to cut down more trees.
  e Low environment score as fossil fuel production/ usage causes environmental problems.
  f It's total score would go up as recycled polystyrene would give a better environment score.
  g You can squirt it into the cavity through a small hole.

35 Movement and energy

1 Work, force, fuel, hot, energy, joules.
2 **a i** 20 J **ii** 2500 J
  b In each case the energy comes from the food the person has eaten.
3 a gets larger **b** greater than **c** decreases
4 a Airliner 6 750 000 000 J; bullet 1125 J
  b The kinetic energy of the airliner is larger than that of the bullet, as it is much more massive. (In fact it is 6 000 000 times more massive than the bullet - so its kinetic energy is 6 000 000 times greater too.)
5 a 2 J **b** 2 J **c** 1.8 J **d** 1.8 J
  e Energy was lost in the impact between the ball and the ground, as the ball was deformed.
6 a 4000 J (4 kJ) **b** 500 J **c** 30 000 J (30 KJ)
  d 200 J

36 Generating electricity

1 **A** The fuel is burnt to give heat energy.
  B This boils the water.
  C Expanding steam turns the turbine.
  D The turbine spins the generator.
  E The generator produces electricity.
2 **A** Sunlight shines on the solar panel.
  B Cold water is pumped into the...
  C The water in the pipes is heated.
  D The heated water passes through...
  E Hot water is produced for heating.
  Anwers A and B could be in either order.
3 Potential, kinetic, turbines, hydroelectric.
4 **A** As the tide comes in, water...
  B The turbines spin generators...
  C As the tide goes out, water...
  D This flows through the turbines...

37 Generation issues

1 **a** A fuel rod contains the uranium or plutonium fuel.
  b A thick concrete case stops the harmful radiation escaping.
  c A reactor core is where the reaction takes place with the fuel in the rods.
  d Liquid sodium in pipes picks up the heat energy from the reactor and carries it out.
2 a Graph correctly plotted.
  b Use higher during the day than night, peaks at breakfast time and dinner time when preparing meals, or any suitable suggestion.
3 a It would take days to start up again.
  b Both hydroelectric plants are switched on.
  c One hydroelectric plant is switched off.
  d Just after 18.30 hr (when demand for power exceeds 8 GW).
4 a 1 GW (1000 MW)
  b Any reasonable suggestion e.g. 50% night, cloud cover, lower angle in winter.
  c 100 MW **d** 25 MW
5 a 100 m
  b 8 GW (8000 MW)
  c 8
  d No. 8 gas-fired power stations would only cost £4000 million, less than £8000 million for the barrage.
  e Gas will run out (non-renewable), tides will not (renewable).

38 Spreading forces

1 **a** This spreads the weight of the vehicle over a larger area, reducing the pressure on the soft ground, so stopping the vehicle sinking into it as far.
  b If the planks are placed on the ice, the weight of the rescuer can be spread over a greater area, so that the thin ice will support their weight.
  c Small area at the point causes the force of the person's finger to be spread over a small area, causing a large pressure, which helps the pin to penetrate the material into which it is being pushed. At the opposite end, the force is spread over a large area, so that the end of the pin is not pushed into the finger.
2 **a** 4 N/cm^2 **b** 50 N/cm^2
3 **a** 113 300 000 Pa **b** 113 N
4 **a** 0.2 m^3 **b** 2400 kg/m^3
  c 0.4 m^2 **d** 12 000 Pa (or N/m^2)
5 25 000 Pa (or N/m^2)
6 a Design B will lift a weight of 720 N using a force of only 90 N, while design A will require a force of 360 N.
  b For each 1 cm the weight is lifted, the left-hand piston in design A must move 2 cm, while the left-hand piston in design B must move 8 cm.
7 144 000 N

39 Matter

1 **a** liquid   **b** solid   **c** gas

2 **a** There are very small forces holding the particles of a gas together, so that they spread out to fill the container they are in.

    b The large smoke particles are bumped into by air molecules, which push the particles randomly in all directions.

3 Answer must include the following: particles move faster and spread apart; the gas takes up a larger volume; the density of this hot gas is therefore reduced; the less dense gas rises up through the cooler, denser gas (*or* it creates an upward force which lifts the balloon.

4 Radiator heats air → heated particles move faster and spread apart, lowering density → Less dense gas rises up through cooler denser gas → As gas moves away from heat, it cools and contracts again → Cooler, denser air sinks → Cool air is drawn in over hot radiator, and so on.

5 2 000 cm³

6 120 m³

7 260 kPa

8 25 cm³

40 Magnets and electromagnets

1 Magnet, north, pole, south, repelled.

2 Unlike poles attract.   Like poles repel.

3 **A** attract   **B** repel   **C** repel
    D attract   **E** attract

4

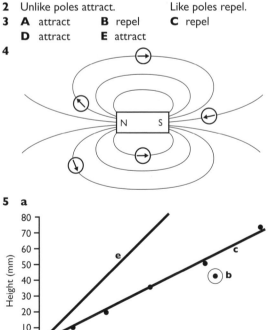

5 **a**

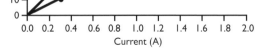

    b See graph   **c** See graph.

d The height jumped increases with the current (is directly proportional to).

e See graph.   **f** Stronger with an iron core.

41 Electromagnets at work

1 Permanent, electromagnets, iron.

2 **a** Becomes an electromagnet.
    b Swings down – attracted.
    c Contacts are pushed together.
    d Circuit complete – current flows, motor turns.
    e Very high current (100 A).

3 The electron is travelling parallel to the magnetic field.

4 **a** When the switch is closed, current…
    The coil becomes an electromagnet.
    The springy steel is attracted…
    This breaks the circuit at the contact.
    The coil loses its magnetism.
    The steel springs back, making…
    The springy steel vibrates backwards…

    b To make it stronger.

5 A variable electrical signal is passed…
    The coil becomes an electromagnet…
    A varying force occurs between the…
    This makes the coil move backwards and…
    The coil moves a paper cone in and out…
    The moving paper cone makes the air vibrate…

42 Motors and generators

1 Motor, electrical, kinetic; generator, kinetic, electrical.

2 **a** No current
    b Reversed current (same size)
    c Larger current
    d More (double) current; reverse direction.

3 **A** When the wire cuts up through…
    B When the wire runs parallel…
    C When the wire cuts down through…
    D When the wire runs parallel…

4 Faster, more, stronger.

5 **a** Spin faster   **b** Reverse direction

6 **a**

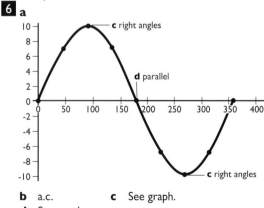

    b a.c.   **c** See graph.
    d See graph.
    e a.c. in the coil passes to two metal rings. The electrical contact to these is made through sprung carbon "brushes" that push against the metal.

43 Using transformers

1 Power, high, low, transformer.

2 Alternating, up, transformer, down.

3 **A** The primary coil produces...

   B The iron core links the field...

   C The secondary coil has an alternating...

4 **a** **i** 200 V   **ii** 100 V   **iii** 4 V

   b 40 V

   c and **d**

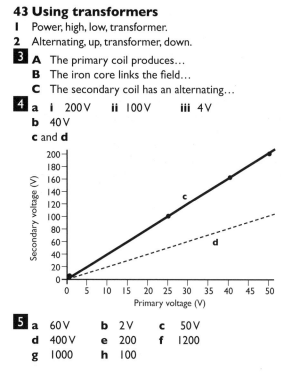

5 **a** 60 V   **b** 2 V   **c** 50 V

   d 400 V   **e** 200   **f** 1200

   g 1000   **h** 100

44 Radioactive substances

1 Protons, neutrons, electrons, nucleus, element, atomic.

2

Particle in the atom	Mass	Charge
proton	1	+1
neutron	1	0
electron	negligible	−1

3 Diagrams like original but ^{22}Na has 11 neutrons, and ^{24}Na has 13 neutrons.

4 **a** 5   **b** 10   **c** boron   **d** 5

   e 11   **f** 8   **g** 16   **h** oxygen

   i 8   **j** 17   **k** 10n, 8p, 8e   **l** oxygen

5 **a** mass number = 32, atomic number = 16

   b mass number = 238, atomic number = 92

   c alpha

45 The best radiation for the job

1 Alpha, beta, gamma, particles, electromagnetic, penetrating, gamma, penetrating, alpha.

2 When there is no smoke, alpha particles can travel from the source to the detector. This keeps the alarm turned off. A small amount of smoke between the source and the detector is sufficient to stop alpha particles reaching the detector. This turns the alarm on.

3 **A** paper   **B** aluminium   **C** lead

   D alpha   **E** beta   **F** gamma

4 **a** As a packet passes through the beam of beta particles, the particles are absorbed and do not reach the detector. Once the packet moves on, particles again

reach the detector. This sequence of pulses of beta particles can be used to trigger a counter.

   b If the detector is placed towards the top of the packet, a packet which is not full of tea will absorb fewer beta particles than one which is full. This provides a way of telling if a packet is full or not based on the intensity of the beta particle beam.

5 **a** $^{236}_{92}$U   **b** $^{241}_{95}$Am, $^{237}_{93}$Np

   c $^{14}_{7}$N   **d** $^{8}_{3}$Li, $^{8}_{4}$Be

   e **i** No change

     ii No change

46 Natural radiation

1 **a** Cosmic radiation comes from space.

   b Radon and thoron are two radioactive gases found in the air.

   c Coal contains small amounts of radioactive materials such as uranium and radium.

   d Radioactivity may be detected using a Geiger counter.

   e Natural radioactive material is taken up by plants and animals which may be eaten by humans.

2 **a** Radiation is produced when unstable atoms decay. Unstable atoms form part of the food, drink and air we take into our bodies.

   b A person high above the ground is exposed to more cosmic radiation than someone on the ground, so a regular air traveller is exposed to more radiation than someone who does not travel by air regularly.

   c Background radiation varies from place to place – for example, it is higher where there are granite rocks. It also varies with altitude (see (**b**) above).

3 **a**

Source	%
rocks and soil	14
food and drink	12
air	51
medical uses	12
cosmic radiation	10
other	1

   b 2.2 units

   c It is slightly more than 10% of the dose from medical sources.

   d Pie chart based on following figures.

Source	Dose (units)	%	Degrees
rocks and soil	0.5	21	75
food and drink	0.26	11	39
air	1.12	47	169
medical uses	0.26	11	39
cosmic radiation	0.22	9	33
other	0.03	1	5
total	2.39		